From Fee Guy & the Boys
XMAS 2005.

Produced and published by
Evegate Publishing Ltd

Producers of
South East Farmer magazine

Written by Peter Tipples

A view from the South

Peter Tipples

The South East's most loved and controversial farming columnist

First published in 2009 by

Evegate Publishing Ltd, Spicer House, Lympne Business Park, Hythe, Kent CT21 4LR

www.evegatepublishing.co.uk

ISBN: 978-0-9563454-0-0

Printed and bound in Great Britain by Stephens and George Print Group

Contents

A view from the South

by PETER TIPPLES

A SELECTION OF MY FAVOURITE ARTICLES IN SOUTH EAST FARMER MAGAZINE

Dedicated to the Tipples family,
Reed Court, Marden

Introduction

A view from the South

by JOHN HARVEY, South East Farmer magazine editor

For readers of South East Farmer, Peter Tipples' column will mean many things – outspoken, occasionally a little acerbic, trenchant and with a knack for knowing what his fellow farmers are thinking. Sometimes, his comments on controversial subjects such as the European Union have driven readers to respond to Peter through the letters pages. But for every one correspondent who doubts his wisdom, there are many others who will line up to defend him – not just in letters, but in telephone conversations, pubs, around dinner tables, and at agricultural shows and ploughing matches across the country. Peter always keeps a close ear to the heartbeat of rural England.

This book is a celebration of Peter's life and his contribution to the stewardship of the English countryside through his articles. More specifically, it fills in much of the biographical detail for those readers who know a lot about Peter already but would perhaps like to know a bit more. By his own admission, Peter is not a townsman. At heart he is a genuine Wealden countryman, completely at home with the animals, birds and trees which surround his home at Reed Court Farm in Kent. He raised his family here with his beloved wife Nancy, and his interests are rooted in the countryside around Marden: farming, of course, especially hops; horses and point to point races; roses; the weather, which has been noted in his diary each day for many years; and sport, particularly cricket. But Peter has also had time for public service through the many organisations he has served with which have links, either direct or less so, to the countryside and farming. It gives everyone at South East Farmer magazine great pleasure to present this full picture of our friend Peter, an outstanding country gentleman.

Reed Court, 2009, planted with Einstein winter whea

In the winter time when we came home from school, we had a couple of ferrets, and we used to go up into the woods with nets to catch the rabbits

My earliest memory was a very nasty accident when a set of wagon rods fell on my head. I remember being carried round from the oast house where this happened into the house where it was found I had a fractured skull.

Luckily, due to the skill of our local doctor – who put my head in ice for several days – I more or less came through it unscathed. Whether it has made me a bit silly, I am not sure – but I don't think so! I was about three or four years old, and was living where I was born at Harts Heath Farm, Staplehurst in Kent which was a family farm of about 280 acres.

About 80 acres was woodland. In the winter time when we came home from school, we had a couple of ferrets, and we used to go up into the woods with nets to catch the rabbits. The ferrets drove the rabbits out of the burrows into the nets. We took the rabbits home, and then sold them in Maidstone market where they made a shilling or two. I love the smell of ▶

WEATHER WATCHING

We used to have a day book in which we noted what we had done, and I started doing that from the moment I came to Reed Court. It was a diary and record of what goes on at the farm. Just before I began writing this, I put down what the barometer reading was today. I have always been interested in the weather, and it has become a habit.

A good friend was talking to me once about the festival we had in the village. She described the festival and she said: "It rained." I said: "It would" and she asked me why I had said that and I said: "Because it always does on that day!" Remarkably enough, the weather has patterns and certain times of the year are good times – so the diary has been useful for that. But it is also very interesting to turn back the pages and see what was going on 30 years ago.

I do not accept theories about global warming, but I will certainly go along with climatic change. I think our weather has become much more Continental than it used to be. We have longer spells of hot weather or cold weather. We used to have more equable weather with more wind. We used to have more spells of soft, kindly weather when it was not too hot and not too cold and it was good growing weather.

▶

My father Sidney was a very highly skilled, good Wealden farmer and hops were the mainstay of the enterprise

woodlands, and spent a lot of time there.

This was a proper farm: my father Sidney was a highly skilled, good Wealden farmer and hops were the mainstay of the enterprise. My father used to say: "The farming side is bread but the hops put the cream on it." Pigs, sheep and bullocks were cared for by up to ten men, there were working horses and it was a mixed farm where all the crops worked in together. The season began with hop growing, followed by the fruit to spray and prune and then the hay making which I always enjoyed.

Harvest was next, and when that was finished, hop picking, which in those days began at the end of August and often went on until the second week of October. Then came fruit picking and the winter was spent mending the wire work in the hop gardens and pruning the fruit. Farmers in those days were farmers, and in the Weald of Kent, nearly all farms were mixed with pigs, sheep, ▶

I think the wind direction has changed, which is one of the most remarkable things. Being a fruit grower, when we have planted trees over the years going back before I came to Reed Court, we always used to stake the trees against the south westerly wind. It doesn't come from there any longer: it is more north easterly, and with that has come a change in the weather. I am a great believer in fresh air, and when the wind is coming from the south west, it is coming off the Atlantic. When it comes from the north east, it is coming off the North Sea – which I reckon is a dead sea! The Atlantic is not a dead sea.

We have much longer spells of one thing or another than we used to. Recently, we have had a very still spell. But there has always been wind in this country. I remember when my children were small and we had au pair girls from Europe. The one thing they always remarked on was how it was always windy here. That is not the case any more: we have more still, intense weather. ■

Today's farmer does have an advantage over older farmers such as myself because he knows how to fill out forms and deal with the endless bureaucracy!

plums, pears, apples, a few cherries, blackberries, currents – and if they were hop growers, they probably had some nice, classy Sussex bullocks in the yards looking out.

Consequently, the farmer had to be adept at knowing what he was looking at. Now, with so many single issue crops on the farms, farmers are not skilled at doing all these things which used to be done. Today's farmer does have an advantage over older farmers such as myself because he knows how to fill out forms and deal with the endless bureaucracy! To do that, he has to be computer literate, which I am not.

My nephew Frank continues to farm at Harts Heath Farm, and it is still a proper farm. He grows hops and fruit and he still keeps sheep. He still looks after the woods, where they spend a lot of the time in the winter shooting pheasants.

Not long after the accident with the wagon rods, my mother Emily unfortu- ▶

CONSERVATION

I am a Wealdsman and the Weald of Kent is a place where there are a lot of woods and trees. I was born and bred on the edge of Marden where we had many woods and I spent a lot of time in them. So I love trees and my daughters sometimes say: "Dad never likes cutting a tree down." All the trees around this house and all those nearby have been planted by me, except for about three. When people talk to me about conservation, I think what have you ever done about it? If anyone asked me the question, I would say I have planted hundreds of trees. That is conservation.

I think the basis of all conservation is a properly balanced countryside with stock, because if you have stock you have fences and hedges, and wildlife can thrive at the bottom of hedgerows. If you have a wide spread of stock with droppings from the sheep and everything else, birds will come into the countryside. All the time you manipulate the countryside mechanically, you do not do what you think you are doing.

I have noted many times in recent years where we have these 15 yard strips around the fields, there is no more wildlife there than there used to be. When we grew hops at Reed Court, we ▶

The children always joined me around the farm. Left to right, myself, Jonathan, Linda and Alison. Jonathan threw the keys out the window

Reed Court Farm, 1961

"Where's Peter?" I was under the table at the time and I said: "Here he is!" and that has often been repeated to me since

nately died and my father subsequently married again. I was brought up in those early days by two aunts and my grandmother at College Road in Maidstone in a little semi detached house called Penryn. One of my clearest memories was my father coming into that Maidstone house and he said to my aunts and my grandmother: "Where's Peter?" I was under the table at the time and I said: "Here he is!" and that has often been repeated to me since.

My uncle had Rugmer Farm at Yalding – not very far from where I am sitting writing this at Reed Court Farm in Chainhurst. I moved there with my aunts and grandmother until I was five and went to Bethany, a private day school at Goudhurst, where I was for eight years. I went back home to Harts Heath Farm whilst I was at school and my brothers and I used to walk up the hill about a mile to the school gates and then back home again. We were always delighted when it rained ▶

always had a few hares because they like the open land of the hop gardens in the winter. We have no hops now and we have no hares. If you have a properly balanced countryside, you will have conservation and flora and fauna without excessive interference. I don't think you can make these places animal friendly: if they don't want to live there, they won't live there. We have one or two fields here that were put over to set aside crops, and there is no more wildlife there than there used to be. ■

Sutton Valence 1938 cricket: Myself, top row, right; John Gray, my life long friend, front row, centre; John Churchill (went on to be Bishop of Liverpool) top row, third left

UB

Russets Hockey Club, 1955, three seasons unbeaten: myself, front row, right

At Sutton Valence, they said I was a bit of a cricketer, and I put in some pretty powerful bowling performances and I batted

because we were taken in the car!

I was middling good at my sums and learning – not brilliant, but enough to keep out of trouble all the time. In 1936, I left Bethany and went to Sutton Valence, a public school. My step mother persuaded my father that we should be schooled properly, and I boarded until 1939.

At Sutton Valence, they said I was a bit of a cricketer, and I put in some pretty powerful bowling performances and I batted. In the first year I was there, John Gray, who became a lifelong friend, was in the colts team with me, and we were playing Kings Canterbury. Now Kings was the bete noire of most of us at Sutton Valence, because Kings all thought they were a bit special. In this particular match, I took six for 18, including a hat trick, and my friend John Gray made 100. Sutton Valence's headmaster was so pleased with us that he loaded me up in a car at the match and took me to the reception for the wedding of my step mother's brother, ▶

CRICKET

My love of cricket continued after my school years and I particularly enjoyed playing for Marden against Rye, two teams, which were mostly made up from farmers. In 1955, there was a devastating hailstorm here at Reed Court Farm at Marden which flattened everything. For years afterwards, the spilled fences looked just as if someone had fired a 12 bore shotgun at them! We didn't have any crops to gather at all except for half a trailer full of oats. There was no farming to do.

It was then my friend Robert Hacking, the captain of Rye, invited me to play cricket with them at any time during the summer. There was nothing at Reed Court to be done, so I took up the offer, and became a very great friend of Robert Hacking.

I made so many friends in sport and my advice to young people is always that if you want to find a good way to mix with other people, play sport – because you will always build up a sound friendship with various people. ∎

Bramling Cross hops at Reed Court Farm

I did actually volunteer for the Royal Air Force before I was hijacked into the Army

which was on the same day.

I could never master French at school – and that is perhaps why I don't like the French, because I could never understand them! When we had the school certificate, as it was in those days, I think I achieved nought for French. I could read the language and I could speak it to a degree, but when the examiner started gabbling away in French, I didn't have the faintest idea what he was talking about – so I had some difficulty answering the questions!

Just before I was 17 on 1 August, I left school and came back, but after a month at home the second world war broke out.

Three years at home were followed by nearly three years in the Army. The reason I was in the Army was that I had two brothers, the first of whom, Bernard, was over 21. Because they had the necessary skills, men over 21 in agriculture were in an exempt occupation from the Army. My younger brother Stuart was too young so as the middle one, I was ▶

WHY I DISLIKE THE EUROPEAN UNION

Back in 1970, I was in an anti common market march in London. I will always remember it because on one side of me was a Communist and on the other side was a Fascist. I was opposed to the European Union from the very beginning. I remember sitting in the dentist's waiting room one day and picking up a magazine which was extolling the wonderful future of Europe. It said British workers would be able to go and work in the German shipyards and painted a very rosy picture.

At the end of the day, my real criticism of the European Union is that I am essentially English. I served in the last war, and in my opinion we fought to preserve our identity. Being a great fan of Winston Churchill, I am always reminded of what he said: "We are of Europe but we are not with Europe," and he said that very clearly.

I was not against the economic background to union, but I was always scared of the political implications. My brother in law was a bomber pilot who was killed and I sometimes used ▶

Cats look down on you, dogs look up to you, pigs is equal

It was assumed that because I had come off a farm, I could drive a tractor and would be a good candidate for the Ordinance Corps

sort of set up for the job. I was not all that keen, but I did actually volunteer for the Royal Air Force before I was hijacked into the Army. I went up to Euston for a health check, and was doing very well until they found I had a perforated ear drum – which went back to the wagon rods falling on my head.

Back home, I was finally summoned to join the Army. I did my initial training on the racecourse at Oadby near Leicester where I was for six months. I was not a good soldier, but I enjoyed the band and the parade ground work. From there, it was assumed that because I had come off a farm, I could drive a tractor and would be a good candidate for the Ordinance Corps. But I was not a very practical man. I understand a cricket bat, hockey stick and tennis racket because there are no working parts in them!

In the end, I celebrated my twenty first birthday at a training centre in Manchester and eventually I was stationed ▶

to wonder for what purpose. We have been gradually taken over by Europeans and people are beginning to wonder where it is all going. It is a bit like the Holy Roman Empire – it has outgrown itself.

I have always been very pro Britain, but it has never been impressed on me what good the EU has done. People say we have never had a war since its formation, and perhaps that is true. But I don't think that is the answer. The politicians have hijacked the union and they are all doing very well out of it. I am not racist, but we should rule ourselves.

Ted Heath, the former Conservative prime minister who took us into Europe, has been the bane of my life. If we had joined Norway and the European Free Trade Association countries, we would have been laughing all the way to the bank. We would have had all the fish and all the oil – what more would we have wanted!

Initially, farming did very well out of Europe. I would agree that it would be very difficult for hill farms to survive today without EU subsidies. But we have been the biggest contributors to the EU budget, and we are only receiving back what we put in. The subsidies have become tighter and tighter, and they have helped other countries as well. Many of the desert regions of Spain, for example, have been irrigated with subsidies to which we have been big contributors and then the crops have come back here! We should continue to live with Europe, but we should not let Europe rule Britannia. ■

It was a lovely starlit night and I stood on the deck as we sailed to a beach near Caen in France

at Camberley just before D Day. I was due to go over with my unit on D Day plus four but somehow I was left behind to join them later, and my orders were "wait until you are sent for." Well, they forgot to send for me, and I was lost for several months!

When I finally had embarkation orders, I went down to Portsmouth as a mere corporal and sitting in the room where we were given orders among all the brass hats – the colonels and the generals. I was in charge of three mobile cranes, and I remember the smell of the diesel on our landing craft crossing the Channel made me quite sick. It was a lovely starlit night and I stood on the deck as we sailed to a beach near Caen in France.

We unloaded the cranes which was a bit dicey because of the steep ramp in about three feet of water. You had to aim for the shore because the metal tracks and the ramp on the landing craft provided no grip.

Loaded on to a transporter with my ▶

DOGS

Because I had sheep, I was always a Border collie man and had one for a long time. After it was mooted that I would be the junior vice chairman of the NFU in Kent, I told my wife I would be away a bit more in the evenings and asked her how she would feel about that. She said if I was going to be away, she would like a big dog! I said I would find one of the biggest for her. Just down the road from Reed Court then was a lady who was important in the Pekingese world, and knew a lot of the people at Crufts. I asked her about Great Danes, and she said she knew a breeder at Rushlake Green in East Sussex.

I went there and we picked one out. He was a dear dog, but he was not a very fit dog, unfortunately. My wife, being a kindly soul, picked him out of the litter because he looked a bit sad. We brought him home and it was a job to rear him but he was the best jumper we ever had. He could jump six feet without much trouble.

He eventually passed on, and we went back to the same breeder. She showed me the litters and I asked her which was the most pushy one. She told me, and he was Parker who came to us in the mid Seventies. From then on, when the Great Danes passed on – sadly, they do not ▶

Corporal Tipples, 14634332

"Ah, Corporal Tipples. Where have you been?" And I replied: "Waiting to be sent for, sir!"

ranes, we began our journey across rance and Belgium through first world /ar country and Caen which the RAF had lown to pieces. From time to time, I was ijacked by various colonels or whoever /ho saw the cranes and wanted some help /ith unloading. Eventually, we reached my nit just outside Brussels and as I marched nto the camp, the commanding officer /as sitting in his bivouac, and said: "Ah, Corporal Tipples. Where have you been?" And I replied: "Waiting to be sent for,

sir!" Just before that, we had parked in the Boulevard de Midi with the transporter and cranes and were making supper in some old cans. Out of a nearby house came a Belgian who asked us in for supper. I said yes, and he had a very pretty daughter, Henriette, which quite fired me up. We were friends before I was moved on.

We went through cities which had literally been razed and were delivering vehicles at that stage, driving them through piles of rubble which had just been bull- ▶

have a very long life span – we sometimes said we would have a look round for another breed. I had made up my mind really anyway that I would not have another breed.

I now have Splash. When Brook, my last Great Dane died in 2004, I decided not to bring a pup up, and contacted the national Great Dane rescue organisation to see what they could do. I well remember writing to them asking for a three year old dog pup with a fawn coat and black mask. Eventually, the lady there – who I know well – 'phoned me up and I went to look at this dog. Well, it wasn't a dog – it was a bitch; it wasn't a fawn coat with a black mask – it was a black and white harlequin; and it wasn't three years old – it was one year old. But I brought Splash home and she is a dear, equable dog. I don't know what I would do without her. ■

23 July 1949, my wedding day
Hopper Levett, wicket keeper for Kent and England is pictured second on the lef

When the Germans broke through the Ardennes, I was close enough to hear the guns going, and it was very snowy

ozed out of the way. It had to be seen to be believed. When the Germans broke through the Ardennes, I was close enough to hear the guns going, and it was very snowy. I finished up at Osnabrück near Hanover in 1945 before returning home. I often think that my unit's next port of call was Japan and, although the atomic bomb was a terrible thing, it didn't worry me at the time because it meant I did not have to go to Japan.

Back on the farm in 1946, there had been little change. We were growing more hops than we had before, and I had always been a sort of public relations man with the hop pickers. It was my job to book the Londoners up every year to come down and live in their huts and pick the hops. When I came back, we had 140 families hop picking. The hop pickers still walked around with big poles in the evening because they were afraid of the dark!

When we began hop picking in 1940, we had no Londoners because the story ▶

MY DEAR WIFE, NANCY

In 1949 I married my dear wife Nancy who had so much to do with the shaping of my family because she was so practical: she could paint, she could garden and she could do nearly everything that I had no idea how to do.

She spent her lifetime in the garden and eventually died outside the back door in the garden. That was very sad. Nancy was in the Land Army but she was never on our farm. She was born and bred in Harmondsworth near Heathrow but her mother was related to the Foreman family in Headcorn in Kent and Frank Day, a Kent farmer, was another distant relative. She stayed in Kent in the summers as a young girl.

I did not meet her until after I had been in the Army. She served in the Land Army on the Berkshire downs and in 1943, her brother David, a bomber pilot, was on his last mission when he was shot down over Hamburg and killed. Beforehand, he was awarded the DFC for landing a Lancaster bomber which had suffered engine trouble with a big bomb on board.

David had done a lot of work in the garden at Ewell in Surrey where they lived. Every time that their mother went into that garden, she thought of David. So they decided to come back to Staplehurst where they had some roots. That was in about 1943.

I had met Nancy once before that playing badminton. I was not impressed with her because she ▶

Nancy with Edward Heath, left and chairman of Hollingbourne rural district counc[...]

Left to right: Pat Minter, Guy Minter[...]
best man at my wedding, myself and Nanc[...]

But then the Blitz started and the next thing that happened was that the Londoners decided that the countryside wasn't too bad after all

ad reached them that the Germans were machine gunning the countryside and) we started hop picking with literally veryone we could lay our hands on. But then the Blitz started and the ext thing that happened was that the ondoners decided that the countryside vasn't too bad after all – and we were verwhelmed with hop pickers! After the second world war, farming /as at the top of the tree because the overnment wanted full production.

We farmed without a lot of interference because our produce was needed. Tom Williams, the then agriculture minister, and Lord Netherthorpe, the president of the NFU, were a good team. Today by contrast, DEFRA ministers insist on telling the farmers what to do!

I settled back into farming quite happily because farming was fun. I was married in 1949 and lived with my new wife, Nancy, in a rented house for a while. Money was still fairly tight for buying ▶

was not very good! But, poor Nancy, she was hit in the eye with a shuttlecock – not by me – and lost the sight in that eye. She spent months in hospital flat on her back.

I knew her on and off. The Army was still in the Staplehurst area then. I remember playing tennis one day when there were a couple of Army officers there and she was definitely keener on them than she was on me! But, eventually in 1947, I finally won the battle and we were married in 1949. Subsequently we had three children: my eldest daughter, Linda; my son, Jonathan; and my youngest daughter, Alison.

Nancy was a very straight forward person and well loved in Marden village. At her memorial service, she was very well supported by so many villagers. She was quite a remarkable woman in so far as she was at home with anyone. In my life, I have done a lot of public work and met the highest in the land. Nancy could always talk to them happily. I remember one occasion when we had a fruit show lunch in Marden and the Duke of Gloucester was the guest of honour. He was sitting next to Nancy at the lunch and said to her: "This is a bit awkward because the table legs are a bit close together. I don't know whether to put my leg one side or the other so that I am close or not so close. I think I had better sit a bit further apart." She would always make them comfortable. I have a wonderful picture of her in my study. Ted Heath, the former Conservative Prime Minister, was the guest at one of our NFU meetings. She is standing there with a cigarette in her hand chatting to him. She was never phased by important people – or not so important people!

She kept me steady and was a great support to me in all the jobs I did. ■

Liverpool Echo, my favourite rose

I had only been to Chainhurst — which is where Reed Court is — once before in my life and I thought it was a right dump!

nother farm, so I used to go to work on my home farm. In 1951, a great friend of my father's suggested we should have a look at Reed Court Farm. I had only been to Chainhurst — which is where Reed Court is — once before in my life and I thought it was a right dump!

In due course, we bought the farm with 60 acres for about £40,000. There were six cottages, a foreman's house and the farmhouse where I am writing this. I moved here in 1951 and have lived here ever since. The farm was not in particularly good order, and needed attention. I well remember — and the diaries I have kept will back this up — putting a lot of manure on the farm. In those days, there was no talk about organic farming because we were all organic farmers. We had loads of feather waste, shoddy, turkey quills and rabbit feet and ears which were all ploughed back into the ground. There is nothing new about organics: it has been rediscovered! Our use of chemical ▶

ROSES

When I came to Reed Court Farm, the first thing I did was to plant roses. I find they are a satisfactory plant to grow because, like hops, they benefit greatly from being looked after properly. People forget that roses are hard working and need plenty of fertiliser.

Before I was married, I was not greatly interested in rose growing. But when I came here they just seized my imagination as being a straight forward plant to grow. Roses do not have complications for someone like me who is fairly bone headed when it comes to working anything out in any detail: roses are an easy crop if you understand them.

I love them because they give such a wonderful span of beauty all through the summer. The first roses come in May and they go on into November: there is always a rose for the button hole! The transition from hop growing to roses is not difficult.

My favourite rose is "Liverpool Echo" which was named after a newspaper in that city. I made a comment once that if the newspaper was as good as the roses, they must have some very good reading there. ∎

This little gang would have known more about hop growing in Kent than anyone else
Hop stringing competition, Weald of Kent. Left to right: Percy Henley (obscured)
William Tipples, Peter Day, Alec Orpin, William Day and Sidney Tipple

With a lady from a Swedish newspape

In those days, we put a lot of the grass seed on with what we called a fiddle, which was shaped like a bow

rtiliser was very minimal.

My father said we had to have some heep here and so in the spring of 1952 we eeded a lot of the fields. In those days, we ut a lot of the grass seed on with what e called a fiddle, which was shaped like bow. The time to seed fields down is te summer when you begin to have dew, nd we put down 100 acres of grass and ery soon after we populated them with omney sheep and Suffolk rams.

Back in the early 1900s, there were 100 acres of hops at Reed Court and in the 1930s the hops were grubbed up and it was all planted with fruit. The fruit was irrigated with underground water mains.

In the early Forties, the hops returned and the difference then was that the oast houses which were used back in the 1920s were still here. So, without too much trouble, it was possible for the man who had the farm before I took it over to put them back into running order. When I came to Reed Court, there were ▶

HOPS AND FRUIT

I have already described how I played a lot of cricket – and I even had a trial for Kent. But I was not good enough – I knew that before I started! In between matches, because I was not afraid to speak my mind, I became county chairman of the NFU, chairman of the cricket and hockey club for 21 years, I captained the mid week cricket side for 25 years, I was secretary and founder member of the Russets hockey club for about ten years and played first eleven hockey for almost 20 years, and in 1964 I became a member of the parish council which I did for 40 years. I was also a governor at Marden primary school for 40 years.

When I gave up my NFU position, I joined the Hops Marketing Board – hops were my real passion – and I was there for 18 years. I tried to be helpful but I didn't pull my punches. Back in the 1980s, there was an explosion of lager beer in the hop industry and there was a variety called Target which was good for brewing lager. I went to a meeting one day with the Brewers Society, one of whom said: "You have to produce these lager hops." I spoke out of turn and said: "Look, we have never let you brewers down yet. If you want these Target hops, you tell us and we will grow them." Subsequently, with the passage of time, we did grow the hops – and, with the passage of time, the brewers didn't want them – which was nothing uncommon at all!

To produce a lager beer, the idea was to have seedless hops. The Weald of Kent was noted for ▶

Bramley apple

For some reason, we decided the peas were not viable and now we just grow rape and wheat at about four tonnes to the acre a lot of the time

Authority, we transferred the whole operation over to arable. Sadly, at that time, we had to abandon the hops, which were going through a lean time.

The next thing was that we were having some difficulty with our sheep management, so we had to give them up, too. We also got rid of our small number of pigs.

We had from time to time picked up odd pieces of land which took the farm up to about 500 acres by the time we went over to cereals. When you have been used to a farm with so many things on it, to go over to what was effectively monoculture was a bit of a bore. We used to grow wheat, rape and peas. For some reason, we decided the peas were not viable and now we just grow rape and wheat at about four tonnes to the acre a lot of the time. We also built a modern grain store and drying plant so that we can do the arable job properly. At times in the summer we used to employ up to 20 people, and now we are back to one! ■

HORSES

After my active cricketing career finished, I began to be interested in horses. My father was a very keen huntsman and he used to ride with the mid Kent stag hounds, which hunted the carted deer.

They used to keep the stags at Boughton Monchelsea and they would let them out and twice a week, one would be taken to where the hounds were meeting, released and given half an hour before being hunted by the hounds. Stag hunting was not for the feint hearted: stags did not look to see where gates were opened. They jumped them. I remember my father came home once and said the stag had jumped 20 five bar gates on Romney Marsh.

Although I used to decry hunting when I was cricketing, it began to get to me that one of my great friends, Robert Hacking – who was captain of Rye cricket club at the time – was a keen horseman. I talked to him one day and eventually acquired a point to pointer and I have been playing about at the game since. I am only a very minor owner. With hunting in my blood, I have been closely involved with the Ashford Valley foxhounds and the Bolebroke beagles. ■

The Farming Scene – viewed from the Weald

MAY 1987: My first article in South East Farmer

This month sees the start of a new regular column written by local farmer Mr Peter Tipples of Reed Court, Marden, Kent.

Peter Tipples farms as a director of S.T. Tipples & Sons Ltd. with his two brothers and two of their sons. They farm in the region of 1,100 acres in and around Marden, Staplehurst and Aylesford, concentrating mainly on hops, cereals, fruit and sheep and cattle in a smaller way.

Peter Tipples was County Chairman of the Kent NFU in 1969-70. He has been a Director of English Hops in its various forms since 1971. He is still an active NFU member and is Chairman of the Marden Fruit Show Society.

His leisure activities include a strong interest in cricket and hockey, and as a conservationist he is actively concerned in the activities of field sports.

Finally, in his own words, he is "an indoctrinated-anti Common Marketeer".

"Although I would not easily admit to being a superstitious type, I have to admit that I view years ending in an odd number with some trepidation.

Accordingly, I surveyed 1987 with misgiving, and when the worst snowdrifts in my memory occurred in January, followed by the worst gale ever in March, my fears seemed to be justified. However, the disasters continued. My point-to-pointer went lame, and in the same week, my Great Dane, Parker, a faithful friend for 11 years, died, and my previous doubts seemed fully justified.

Having survived these traumas, together with a wet miserable start to the spring, the sun is now shining, and hopefully the year will proceed in a less difficult path.

Season of promise

The crops at Reed Court and in the surrounding Wealden areas look generally good, although I am well aware that this is the season of promise, fulfillment is months away.

Rape crops that benefitted from a good drilling time last August look especially well, and together with a good crop of lambs, many farmers will not be dissatisfied with their prospects.

No doubt the possibility of good crops will fill the politicians and the anti-farming lobby with other than friendly thoughts. Nevertheless, the farming community in Britain, who are well aware of the problems of over production, should in no way be over defensive. As the politicians masterminded a ridiculous Common Agricultural Policy, it was no fault of the farmers in this country. The fact that they have used the conditions laid down to increase production was the only sensible approach, bearing in mind all farmers have bank managers! As I travel about the Wealden areas of Kent and East Sussex, I often wonder if some of the farming critics ever come into this lovely countryside. Hedgerows abound, there is of course much land under the plough, but there are woodlands and shaws, and everything one could expect of the English countryside.

Hedgecutting operators have mastered the art of trimming hedges mechanically, without slaughtering them, and the farms generally appear to be under good stewardship.

Economic pressures

There are signs nevertheless, that economic pressures are beginning to take their toll, and corners are having to be cut, in that the jobs that keep the farm tidy are not being done. There is no doubt in my mind, that given a reasonable national prosperity, any government which allows farming fortunes to deteriorate to any great extent, will deserve to be castigated. I do not believe that the general public, who are encouraged, quite rightly, to come more and more into the countryside and onto the farms, expect to be confronted with a shambles. If they find more weeds than cultivated crops growing, they will be the first to criticise the farmers for inefficiency.

If the amount of British money squandered on the C.A.P. was channelled into British agriculture, whether for production or non production, the public would still have good value for their money. **99**

Nostalgic thoughts

As a dedicated hop grower, the approach of September concentrates my mind on hop picking, although this is a much smaller operation than In the hey-day of the hop growing Industry.

One's thoughts turn nostalgically to days when the Weald of Kent was the home of the Fuggle hop and few farmers would have been without some hop gardens. Marden is now, I believe, down to seven hop growers. It is somewhat ironic that the demise of the Fuggle which was brought about by the disease, verticillium wilt, was only the forerunner of other problems.

Pale apology for beer

With the general public now consuming an ever increasing quantity of that pale apology for beer, known as lager, traditional aroma type hops like Fuggles are fighting what appears to be a losing battle. The only salvation one can hope for, is that the male population will return to drinking a man's drink – bitter, and leave lager to the ladies. It will be a sad day, if the time comes, when the traditional English Pub no longer serves proper beer.

Whilst on the subject of beer, I note the brewer's intentions of increasing the price yet again – due, it is said to increasing rates. It is certainly not due to the price of

hops, and of course hop growers, unlike brewers, are supposed not to have overheads!

Apple marketing

Last month I made some uncomplimentary remarks on the general state of apple marketing and as the season unfolds matters do not improve. The wholesale markets seem to vie with each other as to who can achieve the lowest prices, and at the time of writing, Discovery, now at last fit to eat, is barely worth picking. I wonder if we will ever succeed in persuading the housewife to pay big money for English apples when they are fit to eat, as opposed to paying high prices for early season apples that are only fit for horses, with strong teeth.

Talking marketing, I suppose am not alone in experiencing frustration the time it takes for th proceeds of my fruit t actually arrive in m bank. Livestock is pai for almost immediatel fruit being a perishab crop, should somehow into the same category.

Golf courses and cricket pitches

Having had a mini he wave in mid August, t weather seems to ha reverted to normal and t combines stand silent in t fields, as grim forecasts a made about the quality ar quantity of the grain cro Fortunately all is not gloo as the sheep farmers ha enjoyed a good trade f their lambs. Hopefully lam production will not exce demand too quickly, for in t Utopian countryside of t future, animals of some so will have to eat the grass; I not believe the entire land c be covered with golf cours and cricket pitches. Myse having reached the end my usefulness as a cricket I can only see a future as umpire, or devoting more tir to my roses, and who know perhaps the next bright id will be to cover the land wi roses, if the rose can reco from the stigma of being us as a political emblem!

WEALD OF KENT PLOUGHING MATCH ASSOCIATION

Sponsored by

For yearly dates and ploughing match locations go to
www.wkpma.co.uk

9 Ploughing Classes	Gymkhana	Trade Show
Horse Ploughing	Clay Pigeon Shooting	Bar & Refreshments
Steam Ploughing	Terrier Racing	Further Attractions

Adults £5, Concessions £2.50, Under 16s FREE. FREE CAR PARK.

Images supplied by Camera-Craft

Change of scenery essential

Passing the Marden cricket and hockey ground the other day, I was reminded of the changing seasons. The cricket square was under renovation and the hockey goal posts were in place. This caused me to reflect on the many happy carefree days spent on sports fields, when my only worries were presented by the opposition sides.

I was always fortunate in being able to leave my troubles at home, firstly because I was a single minded player, and secondly because my wife was generally capable of dealing with most eventualities that might crop up in my absence; this made me wonder if the intense pressures of farming today, causes farmers in general to be less able to get the necessary change of scenery, so essential to any active businessman.

Suicide, I understand, is more common amongst farmers than in many other business professions and I suggest this is because farmers are becoming so totally involved in their farming operations.

With most farms running on a minimum labour force, farmers, young and old, find themselves involved in general jobs about the farm, that years ago, a boy who had recently left school, would have done. This pressure has no doubt

not only had an effect on the farmers ability to partake in sporting activities, but perhaps more importantly in his ability to give time, to the NFU, The Country Landowners Association and other organisations responsible to his industry. Even more important still, farmers used to play a leading part in local government, on district councils where their commonsense views made a useful contribution. Nowadays the farming voice is being lost increasingly, to the detriment of all concerned. This is an unhappy state of affairs and unless farming is better supported by whatever government is in power, the trend will continue to accelerate and the country and the countryside as a whole, will

be the poorer.

Returning to more immediate problems, the saga of the Moulin wheat disaster rolls on. Whilst I have every sympathy for those growers who have suffered severe financial losses, most of us who grow wheat have been caught up to some degree, and although I can understand that retribution seems to need to be exacted, it does appear to me, that given all the circumstances, the weather was the villain of the piece and it will be difficult to gain compensation from On High!

A problem facing apple producers, and to which they should be giving urgent attention, is, by what means the price of apples in the market place can be translated to the shelves of the supermarkets. Whilst in a local supermarket, Discovery apples were retailing at 42p per pound, wholesale prices would have been 10-15p per pound, if saleable, and I am talking about the third week in September.

Not only do I feel the public are being ripped off; the high prices asked, must inhibit the demand. There is of course a simple explanation, farming is about production, supermarkets are about profits.

With Robert Wickham, playing for Marden. I was skipper of Marden Midweek for 25 years

Farming folk – resilient and optimistic

It seems an age since the occasion of the Weald of Kent ploughing match in Marden held on a beautiful sunny warm early October day. I remember thinking what a wonderfully resilient and optimistic body of people farming folk are.

After a season in which crop-wise, there has been little joy, here they were, busy making plans for another season, assuming it had to be better than the one just passed. Little did anyone know that their optimism was about to be tested to the full and that devastation was just round the corner.

The night of 15th/16th October was something we shall never forget, and the sight that met our eyes at dawn on Friday morning was unbelievable. No section of farming escaped, from the milk producers who could not cool their milk, to the fruit growers who literally had their fruit trees blown away – at least the milk producers still had their cows! This is not to mention damage to farm buildings and trees in general.

It is interesting to note the public's concern at the loss of trees, which are part of our landscape, and their natural sadness to the damage of Kew Gardens and other national parks is understandable. However there seems to have been remarkably little aware-

ness that the greatest loss of trees has been on landowners and farmers property. Not only do the farmers share the sadness at loosing their trees, they also have to bear the cost of clearing them up.

There seems to have been a lack of urgency in high places to the plight of farmers in the south east of England, and I am sure I can be forgiven for thinking that had this natural disaster occurred in some remote part of the Commonwealth, a disaster appeal would have been quickly set up. As one who still firmly believes that Britain's membership of the EEC is a total irrelevance, I suggest Mr McGregor spends a little less time in Brussels and gets on

his bike and studies conditions in the south east; what he sees could well be a preview of the future farming scene, if the Government does not support agriculture more enthusiastically. There is no doubt that the true heart of a country is in its inner countryside, not in its inner cities.

With over 7" of rain so far this month cereal drilling is far behind schedule and only a very fine spell of quiet weather can prevent a backlog building up for the spring.

Despite the traumas at Reed Court, and there have been plenty, Leo continues to grow, and at approaching 6 months old, he has just scaled 90lbs.
Leo was my Great Dane then

Nancy with Leo in 1993

Nothing in common with the average European

After what has been the wettest autumn and winter in my memory, a lot of questions will need to be answered during the coming growing season, not only for crops but lambing ewes as well.

With virtually no frosts, the waterlogged ground has not received the customary benefits from being frozen, and although as February draws to an end and the ground begins to dry up, the sight of tractors bogged down in fields, will not I believe, be an uncommon sight, as farmers tend to push ahead with cultivations in advance of suitable conditions. Much of the later sown cereal crops are at present showing considerable signs of distress even where there is a decent plant, for with the constant waterlogging root growth will have been minimal. Lambing ewes have equally had a hard time, spending too much time standing up and too little time dry. All in all farmers will hope for an equable season with no extremes, and can only hope that the elements will be kind to them even, if the Government is not.

Help

Thinking of help, which is generally lacking from Government sources, it seems extraordinary to me that the APDC should generously donate £100,000 of fruit / grower's money to the Government, albeit, through ADAS. I believe that at this stage expensive advice from ADAS to growers in the aftermath of the hurricane is premature, better to wait until late summer to see the effects, in the meantime I think the money would be better spent cheering us up in the pub!

Conned into voting

In recent months I have held back from a general attack on the Common Market, useless though that organisation might be, when a regional disaster occurred within its boundaries, considerable aid would no doubt be forthcoming and the hurricane presented a good case. However it would seem that the EEC is as unhelpful to us as usual. Reading the obituary of John Cherrington who has recently died, it states that "He was always fiercely opposed to the Common Market long before it became fashionable to be so". I would not claim to be even the poor man's John Cherrington, but I believe my opposition to that European catastrophe would go back just as far. It has never ceased to amaze me how farmers and the public in general, could ever have been conned into voting to join such an organisation.

Poorer by the year

As an island race we have nothing in common with the average European, and it is not surprising that we are constantly irked by the steady stream of bureaucratic nonsense that emanates from Brussels. Harmonisation is the name of the game, even the extra hour of daylight we enjoy during the summer evenings is apparently now under threat. Before Britain's entry into the EEC, farming in the British Isles had a good name, now due to a system where more and more money is poured into the CAP the farmers get poorer by the year, whilst the bureaucrats and market manipulators get steadily fatter, and then the farmers shoulder the blame. Rather like the NHS the money goes in at the top but leaks out at the sides before reaching the intended recipients. Of our leaders in recent times, Edward Heath was, I believe, the only one who ever truly believed in the concept of the EEC and his demise was swift.

Fraud in the EEC is a sick joke

One of the talking points by politicians and business men in recent weeks, has been the degree of fraud within the EEC and CAP, in particular.

In a bureaucratic organisation such as the EEC, the opportunities are rife for manipulators to exploit the system. I suppose, if the farmers in the UK were enjoying the proceeds of fraudulent dealings and laughing all the way to the bank, they could afford to be indifferent to the situation.

But, as they have not been worse off in 50 years, it is a somewhat sick joke. Although little was made of it farming-wise, the result of the Richmond by-election was a telling commentary on the fortunes of farmers. No doubt there are those who would say the near bankrupting of British agriculture is a small price to pay for peace in Europe.

On the domestic scene, there is much gnashing of teeth in the higher echelons of power in the fruit farming industry over the adverse vote for the continuation of the Apple and Pear Development Council.

A leading member of the NFU's apple and pear committee said: "The committee were shell shocked by the result." I can only add that I am staggered they were shocked.

A brief sortie into the sticks, where the fruit is grown, would have soon discovered the disenchantment of many growers with the activities of the APDC and a straight yes/no vote on its future was always in doubt.

One can only hope that other committees at NFU headquarters have more understanding of producers' views; otherwise it would appear McKindsey did not come a moment too soon!

Since it would seem that the funding of research into fruit farming is everyone's main concern, it is to be hoped the leaders of the fruit industry will stop moaning when democracy takes its course and organise a system to fund research – as the hop growers have done since Peter Walker dealt their marketing board a mortal blow some years ago.

In the immediate future, there are many fruit growers in the Weald who will miss the advice and visits of Podger Norton, of Heath Engineering Works. Podger, who died in the winter, was an undisputed expert on the pests and diseases of fruit and hops.

An unassuming, quiet man, he was also a great countryman, his especial joys being shooting and fishing. He will be greatly missed in many ways.

Now that the proposed route of the new rail link has been announced, it is to be hoped that the Kent County Council will have nothing to do with it until the Government – who made the decision leading to the need for the new rail link – accept their responsibilities to fund whatever is necessary.

As March draws to an end and talk about the destruction of the ozone layer continues, I wonder if much has changed. My records show that over the years the arrival of the Cheltenham National Hunt Festival means the advent of very adverse weather.

This year has been no exception and, although not much in the farming industry seems to be blooming, it was heart warming that Desert Orchid was...

Meeting the Duke of Gloucester at a Fruit Show luncheon

1986 Fruit Show: Left to right, Lord Selbourne, Lord Belsted , myself and Lord Tonypandy

Voters give Europe thumbs down

June this year brings voting for the greatest quango ever invented.

I refer, of course, to the EEC and the Euro elections in particular. The fact that probably not much more than a quarter of the electorate will trouble to vote will be regarded with little significance, although it amazes me that people seem happy to acquiesce while busybodies in Brussels continue to meddle in our affairs.

A straight Yes or No vote on Britain's continued membership would bring out the voters who stay away from voting for ineffective politicians. I am sure the people of Kent would find no difficulty in voting No, because, without question, our continued membership of the EEC means the decimation of Kent as we know it.

Ironically, a financial expert writing in a Sunday newspaper was of the opinion that Britain's trading future lies with America!

On the subject of voting, odd things are happening in the apple growing world. Having had a poll for the future of the APDC, in which a majority voted against, certain leading bodies decided the result was not to their liking. They initiated a further phoney poll in the hope of getting a better result.

It does not seem to occur to these people that Mr Average

Grower wants a bit of democracy – he wants to pay towards research and development, but he wants a fair say in what goes on, without the big boys spending his money for him.

Crops in the Weald are looking in fine fettle at present and, following a dry winter, a much wetter April than usual has put everything right. Now, with the very warm weather, it is difficult to find crops that look other than promising. Although May has been very dry, an equable June will, I believe, ensure good crops.

For me, May has seen the end of 18 years as a member of first the Hops Marketing Board and then English Hops Ltd. When I joined in 1971 we had an organised industry in which the growers were earning fair rewards for supplying the

brewers with what they wanted.

It was, I believe, an entirely satisfactory situation and I am sad to leave the corridors of power – if that's what they are – at a time when the hop growing industry was never more fragmented, with growers' financial returns at a low ebb.

The brewers, in the meantime, have never had it so good and it is to be hoped that growers will unite in trying to get a fair share of the profits that the brewers are undoubtedly making.

To finish on a really happy note, my horse, with whom I am in partnership with Robert Hacking was a convincing winner at the United Hunts meeting at Folkestone. Leo would, indeed, have been stretched to catch him on this occasion.

I have been told that the surest way to break up a friendship is to be partners in a racehorse. The fact that our relationship has always been totally harmonious says much for the close ties built up on the cricket field at Rye many years ago.

Robert, of course (unlike me), does know a bit about racehorses, having ridden nearly 200 winners in his time.

Counting the cost of a hot summer

Reading Mrs Thatcher's speech at the Royal Show, I detected a slight softening of her attitude to the farming industry.

Now, whether this is because the Government realise how successful they have been in giving a hard time to farmers, or whether information has filtered through that many of the food mountains have disappeared and harvest prospects do not look too abundant, only time will tell. Perhaps, the Government just needs friends?

With harvesting of winter barley already under way, yields of cereals are difficult to assess. Some of the barley crops already harvested are light and, in many cases, spring sown cereals will not cover costs.

One of the interesting climatic results of this very hot summer is that the excessive heat has pushed crops on towards maturity at such a speed that plants have not made the necessary structure to carry a big yield.

Also, with crops so far advanced, the normal theory (especially in the case of hops) that a reasonably wet July could ensure a good crop, may be wrong this year. Certainly, winter cereals have passed the point where rain would do much good.

The warm weather, despite the thunderstorms of early July, has dried up many pastures. Dairy farmers are finding things difficult and it remains to be seen if a shortage of keep will affect the forthcoming store lamb sales.

On the subject of sheep, the Ministry of Agriculture has at last seen some sense in making compulsory dipping an annual task. Unfortunately, decreeing that this hard labour has to take place in the autumn does not help much, for many of us will still dip in the summer in the cause of good flock management.

One of the continuing contradictions in this age of "The Green", when concern is being voiced about the use of nitrates and its getting into the water supplies, is that the Government and the river authorities take such a lax attitude to the continued pollution of our waterways.

The discharges of raw sewage into our rivers is a disgrace, as is the dumping of toxic chemicals into the rivers. And I fear neither the Government nor the river authorities can be taken seriously in respect of protecting our environment if this ecological disaster is allowed to continue a moment longer.

Remedy

I note that soundings are to be taken to find out public opinion in respect of aligning our clocks with those on the Continent.

I hope that, of the many inconveniences that have befallen us as members of the EEC, this one can be successfully fought off. In spite of the view put out by big businessmen that they can only do business with their Continental counterparts during four hours of the day, I have a simple remedy for them – start work earlier and do not spend most of the middle part of the day at lunch or in the pub.

I am sure country folk find plenty of hours of daylight during the summer and I am usually pleased when it gets dark.

Let us hope that when this matter comes up for public debate, the reasonings of commonsense will not be overruled. In this age of vocal minorities, it often seems there are too many dragons to be slain – and too few St. Georges to do it.

Food is best when it is fresh

Many people will not look back on 1990 as being one of the better years.

Farmers will generally have seen their indebtedness to the banks continue to rise, Fred Barker excepted, of course, and, in fact, nearly all industries involved in production have suffered to the point of insolvency.

Even the money manipulators have come unstuck, Eric Saunders and Azil Nadir being two classic examples.

And, finally, Mrs Thatcher eventually paid the penalty of paying too much attention to foreign affairs and too little to her potential voters.

After 11 years of sterling service, she shared the same fate as an ever greater Prime Minister of this century – Winston Churchill – who received equal thanks after the 1939-45 war!

My wish for 1991 will be that it will be a year in which common sense and perspective will triumph over dogma.

The environment seems to be number one in everyone's mind, so perhaps this would benefit from a common sense view.

Firstly, to acknowledge that nothing can really be done to enhance the countryside, without the active help of the farmers, who can only do their part if they are financially stable.

Next, perhaps organic farming could be viewed in its true perspective, that it will be a nine day wonder, and, although chemical inputs into farming will no doubt decline, there is no proof that organically produced food is beneficial to the human body.

Common sense tells you that the food is best when it is fresh.

And so on to the question of hunting.

Most people who oppose hunting know very little about the subject and would do well not to disclose their ignorance.

If hunting is stopped, the country will become decimated of its wildlife, but in turn, who will stop the gangs of thugs roaming the countryside at night, with their torches and lurchers, killing everything that moves?

Not, I fear, the police, who are activated to persecute motorists for almost any reason, whilst the country is beset by ever increasing burglaries and a general breakdown of law and order.

If ever there was a case for viewing matters in perspective, this is an obvious example.

And, perhaps, my last wish would be that the super market bosses would pa a little less attention to th ringing of the tills and trea their suppliers in a civilise manner and their customer with consideration.

And so on to 1991.

I look forward to the Point to-Point season starting nex month. Whether or not I ca afford a point-to-pointer an a big dog, I do not know. Bu if they and a loyal famil prevent me from telephonin the Samaritans, I sha continue to spend my har earned savings as I wish.

Perhaps one day farmin will get better so then I ca put some more money bacl into the kitty!

Cambridge might even wi the boat race again!

Ollie winning the restricted at Charing in 1995 in the fastest time of the day

Farming's decline affects whole village community

Recently my own village of Marden featured in a television news item concerning the decline of the village shops.

Whilst there is no doubt that the dreaded supermarkets contributed to this unfortunate fact, people are apt to ignore the underlying reason. Quite simply, this can be attributed to the sad state of the farming industry.

Forty years ago, Marden would have had many hop growers, now the village is down to six. There were many acres of big apple trees and most farmers kept sheep, pigs and bullocks. Now there are virtually no pigs, few cattle and even sheep are under threat. All these enterprises demanded a high level of labour.

Now most of the cottages are sold to people who have no interest in agriculture and probably little interest in their local village.

This adds up to the demise of local life, as urban dwellers impose their views. Marden used to boast one of the best hardware shops in the Weald, which together with its agricultural enterprise brought people into the village from all over the area.

My plea to those who sit in high places and impose their rule, is, please note what is

happening before it is too late. The villages will become deserted places in the daytime and if some factions have their way, the traditional sports enjoyed in our countryside will be stopped.

Do the public as a whole want to see villages without shops and a countryside where the hunting horn is no longer heard? I doubt it.

Since my apparent one-man assault on the supermarkets about a year ago, I seem to have attracted many allies.

Nevertheless, it is interesting to note the way the establishment views matters, when we have Alistair Grant, Chairman of Argyll Foods and boss of

the Safeway supermarket who flou the law and ope on a Sunday, bein given a knigh hood!

I note that eage beavers in th health authoritie are suggesting tha food prepared b our WI ladies an other goodly peop who offer food various local fun tions from their ow kitchens, may fir themselves prevente from doing their goo work, until their pre ises are adjudged conform with publ health requirements.

At times I think th world has gone complete mad. As I see harrowin pictures of undernourishe people in third world cou tries, with a multitude of fli crawling over them, I wond what kills them – salmonel or starvation!

The continuing dry weath is wonderful for getti on with all necessary far work, but unless Februa fill-dyke lives up to its nam many water authorities w be viewing the future wi apprehension.

For Leo watchers, aft the Christmas festivities, tipped the scales at 10 stone pounds.

L'Aimant

We need fire and brimstone

FEBRUARY 1993: Farmers did do something about it

At a recent meeting of our Parish Council, the business turned to the environment and the state of the countryside.

A fellow Parish Councillor remarked how sad it was to see the countryside deteriorating and looking unkempt with set-aside, and inquired, "Can't the farmers do something about it?' An innocent enough remark, but it reinforced my belief that the general public has no idea of the farming industry's problems. Unfortunately farmers seem to have lost the ability to speak up for themselves.

The January meeting of the Kent N.F.U. executive was attended by a disgracefully poor number of delegates and those there seemed to have nothing to say.

Turning my mind back to 1970, the farmers then decided they had had enough and under the able leadership of Henry Plumb, took action.

Towns were blocked, markets were closed and the public were in no doubt that the farmers were making a point.

Kent N.F.U. executives in those days were enlivened by the likes of my good friend Bill Henderson, of Ash, who, sadly, died last summer and who had no difficulty in making his view abundantly clear, whether it was on the state of farming, or that dreadful lot who dwelt on the other side of the Channel!

Somehow or other, the farming industry has got to engender a bit more fire and brimstone, because even if the economy picks up, farming has its own special problems.

With the exception of coal (and a change of heart seems imminent there) farming labours under the burden of being told it produces too much and in the shake out from the GATT proposals, our Continental neighbours will get more than their share if we do not stop them.

Farmers must not be constrained fro forcefully puttin their case; there a view they shou keep their hea down, as with s aside, because th are being paid f doing nothing. Th nonsense has be originated by the EE and supported by o own Government: a it is not of the farmer making.

The rainfall in 1992 f the first time in five yea reached the tradition average of 26 inche Although it will seem wet year in many peopl minds, it should be remer bered that the first six mont were very dry with only 8 inches of rain, including very dry, hot June. The ne six months yielded 17 inches.

As I write, January seems be continuing to be wet ar wild, and farmers have no had enough of it – even if t water companies have not!

By the time this isst reaches you we shall be on t threshold of our area poin to-points, and I look forwai to many days of enjo ment amongst good-nature people, enjoying the countr side and the horses. Long m it continue!

SHORTLAND STRUCTURES LTD

STEEL FRAMED BUILDINGS · CLADDING & ERECTING

A summer of big yields – and prices

Weatherwise, the South East has seen a generally good farming summer.

Although the weather has been rather unsettled, often being broken up by frequent thunderstorms, sunshine and rain have usually come at the right time.

A dry March saw a good lambing and a wet April set the crops growing. May was a month of very mixed weather. June had hot spells at the beginning and end of the month, making life difficult for soft fruit growers.

July started very hot, but soon became very unsettled with rain coming at just the right time for hop growers. St. Swithin's Day was rainy and, as expected from local folklore, the summer has never really settled again.

However, the first three weeks of August were warm and harvesting was carried out without too much trouble. September has again been unsettled and hop and fruit growers will be hoping not to be caught in the aftermath of any hurricanes.

All this adds up to good yields in most crops, with hops being well up to average and of good quality. With a much improved trade for both lambs and cattle and a steady cereal trade, the farming industry is probably in better heart than for some years.

However, as a grower of a very reduced acreage of apples and pears, I cannot help but view the future of the hard fruit industry with concern.

While certain elements of the advisory services persist in issuing statements on the lines that fruit will not keep this year (when has there ever been a year when someone has not said this?), the biggest problem seems to be between wholesale and retail prices.

While William pears were selling in late August on the markets for about 10p per lb, they were on sale in the shops as far apart as Sheffield and Southampton at about 40p per lb. Bramleys, likewise, were struggling around 10p to 14p and on sale at about 35p, while Discovery were 45p!

Better marketing? I still wonder what that is.

So much for the actual farming operations, but what about our critics? There is hardly a week goes by without some mention of farmers destroying the flower meadows or chopping hedges.

What utter hypocrisy. In my opinion, the two biggest destroyers of the countryside and its villages are the motor car and the supermarket chains.

I firmly believe that the internal combustion engine is the biggest polluter of the atmosphere, but when increased car sales were announced for August, there was general jubilation in government circles. More cars mean more roads mean less hedges and more beauty spots destroyed.

So, where do the supermarkets come in? Quite simply by their efforts to destroy the village shops.

With Sainsburys' pre-tax profits on course for £1 billion in the year 1995-1996 and for the current year of £73 million do these organisations need to send their buses into the villages to solicit customers?

Supermarket bosses often make noises about helping to maintain the countryside. As a start, I suggest, they withdraw their buses.

Finally, with fox hunting about to begin again, I wonder why the hunting fraternity are usually so eminently respectable and peace loving whereas the antis are the exact opposite!

THERE'S ALWAYS A TUB OF GOLD AT THE END OF OUR RAINBOW

CRYSTA LYX®

CALTECH HELPLINE 016973 32592

EXTRA HIGH ENERGY
Ideal for flushing ewes, in-lamb ewes, breeding tups, growing/finishing lambs at grass for optimum fertility.

CATTLE BOOSTER
Balances winter forages and summer grass.
For all youngstock, dairy or beef; breeding bulls; lactating cows or sucklers on summer grass.

CATTLE HIGH-MAG
Helps maintain normal blood magnesium levels to reduce the risk of hypomagnesæmia (staggers/grass tetany).

CALFLYX EASY BREATHER
Helps reduce coughing and respiratory problems in calves, young cattle and housed sheep.

PRE-CALVER
Helps support and maintain a strong, healthy immune system, replenishes trace elements and vitamins pre-calving, optimises health and vigour of both cow and calf.

OPTIMUM
Formulated to provide selected KEY nutrients to help stimulate appetite and dry feed intakes in freshly calved cows

ORGANYX PLUS
Fully approved, 100% organic feed suitable for year round feeding to all cattle and sheep.

GARLYX
Produces an invisible screen over the animal's body to help repel insect bites while optimising forage digestibility and intake.

STANDARD
High-Mag for sheep. Ideal for mixed grazing systems in spring to reduce the risk of hypomagnesæmia (staggers/grass tetany)

Having to live with the pain of slaughter

As the controversy over the export and transport of livestock gains in momentum, unpleasantness and intimidation, it is perhaps the time for those ordinary folk who join the demonstrations, to stand back and study a few facts.

We know, of course, that the anarchists who motivate the demonstrations are not interested in either reason or law and order.

Firstly, the average human being is a meat eater and, to this end, animals are reared and, however unfortunate, they are eventually, mostly slaughtered.

Secondly, before their eventual end, they have to be loaded on to lorries and transported to abattoirs – which, like crematoriums, are not particularly cheerful places.

Thirdly, these supposedly good people seem to forget that a pleasant countryside is in many cases dependant on a thriving livestock industry, that allows farmers to rear their animals under the best possible conditions.

Fourthly, most livestock producers want the best for their animals, and like me, I am sure, are generally sorry when the animals they have reared and cosseted, leave on the final journey.

So what is to be done?

An outbreak of common sense would be helpful for a start, and whilst most of us do not condone veal crates and tethered stalls for sows, it takes time to eradicate these practices. In the meantime, the livestock industry must not be allowed to go to the wall.

It should be remembered that the Continentals do not view animals in the same elevated light in which they are viewed in this country; also be noted, that the export of livestock is important to the country's finances, although it goes without saying, that we should be doing everything possible to improve animal care once these animals have arrived on the other side of the channel.

And finally, I will repeat what I said some months ago, animals suffer initial stress on being removed from their normal surroundings, wherever they may be going. What must be insured is that their transportation must be above reproach.

Turning to more normal matters, we have just endured the wettest January I can remember, and at last, after a couple of dry days at the end of the first week in February the mud is just beginning to solidify! The sheep have had a dreadful time, although the mild weather has just kept the grass on the move.

On the horticultural front many people have been surprised by the extent of the take up of the new grubbing grants, which has exposed the profitability of fruit growing.

The supermarkets, who are quick to shed crocodile tears over inhumanely produced meat, might well consider giving their suppliers, whether they are meat producers fruit growers or nurserymen, better prices for their products and pay for them a bit quicker.

The recent cheerful picture of point-to-pointers in action reminds me that the South East season is about to begin.

My own horse, after a year's inaction through injury, is hopefully back to fitness, and I look forward to some good relaxing days amongst pleasant company, when I hope my blue and yellow colours will show up on occasions.

With Leo at my feet as I put my thoughts on paper, I look forward to a good spring and a productive summer and hope that some of the problems facing our industry can soon be resolved and farmers can get on doing what they are good at – FARMING!

Good day at the races
– if you own a winner

The Easter Saturday Point-to-Point at Charing was a most enjoyable day for me. My horse Rustic Ramble, won the second race in the fastest time of the day.

Superbly ridden – as always – by Paul Hacking, he was gently eased through the field, taking the lead three fences out and staying on to beat the favourite in a strong finish.

My friends seemed almost as delighted as I was, and with the bookmakers being reasonably generous, they would, I hope, have comfortably covered their entrance fee.

A good day at the races especially if you own a winner and even if you back one, does much to ease the trials and tribulations of farming, which is in itself, a considerable gamble.

In an endeavour to get more people into the countryside and to understand it better, the NFU is encouraging all local branches to hold an open day on a farm, under the banner of Welcome to the Countryside.

As one who has had a farm trail for many years, I support the idea, but sometimes wonder if we really get the message across; that farming is often a lonely and poorly rewarded occupation.

According to the NFU publicity department, visitors to the farm will not want to know of the acute problems

facing many farmers and it is here that I would differ strongly from some of the desk bound officials of headquarters public affairs department.

Of course I would agree that people would not wish to come on to a farm for an enjoyable days outing, to be confronted by a farmer bemoaning his lot. On the other hand, I sometimes think we undermine our own case. I am sure any farmer who holds an event on his farm, hopes fervently that it will be a fine day and literally everything in the garden will be lovely, so that as the guests depart, they think what a wonderful day it has been in the idyllic countryside.

I believe it to be no bad thing, to 'point out that the sun does not always shine, and quite often the various farming

operations are carried c under atrocious condition Furthermore, it could added, that although ma farmers live in substant houses, these do in fact with the job and were built most cases when farming w the premiere industry in t country.

Finally, it could be gen pointed out that when N Blair recently said that, in t event of a Labour Governme being in control, only peop who were earning in excess £30,000 per annum, wou be targeted for extra taxatic not too many farmers wou have choked on their eggs a bacon, as they read that sta ment!

The days when we had proper spring seem to have go – perhaps I dwell too much my boyhood. But once we us to have warm soft Aprils w pleasant growy showers. Th year has been a good examp of an unkindly April. Genera dry and often cold, we ha had three swingeing frosts the 19th, 20th and 21st. T full extent of the damage is to be revealed. A further vaga of this spring has been t dramatic variation in tempe tures. On April 26th the t temperature was 56°F, on M 3rd it was 80°F.

After the very wet wint a nice, warm rain is bad needed by all crops.

Baroness Trumpington gave Nancy a kiss and then looked at me and said "I'd better give him one too!"

An old dog with an eye for the fillies!

As August is the month when all the world except the farming community seems to be on holiday and also begins with my birthday, perhaps I can be forgiven for starting my monthly contribution on a light hearted note.

Whilst watching the annual out of season cricket match between point-to-point owners and Jockeys, I was approached by a friend who was concerned that my July article made no mention of either my dog or my horse. For those readers who are interested, I can reassure them that both are in extremely good fettle. Brook continues to grow and at 120lbs, and with teeth that seem to be able to chew everything, has all the makings of a fine example of a Great Dane. Back to the cricket, which was necessarily not too serious, the occasion was further enhanced by the presence of several pretty girls in pretty dresses, even if in some instances, they were somewhat minimal. Does this mean the retreat of the dreaded jeans. I, hope so, because even with advancing years, my Leo background will not allow me to fail to notice the more attractive facets of life!

Before being accused of undue frivolity, I will return to the more mundane matters

of life, notably the weather. An interesting thought has occurred to me, that unless we are about to experience easily the driest year of my life, we are set for a very wet autumn and early winter. As we approach mid-August, even though the weather is becoming unsettled, rainfall at Reed Court, to date for this year, is about 9.1/3". Average rainfall being about 26", one does not have to be a mathematician to work out that in four and a half months a lot of rain has to fall. Livestock farmers are of course feeling the most dire effects of the dry weather and keep, in my part of the world, is a most non-existent. Although it has to be remembered that there was bountiful grass last autumn. For sheep farmers it has been

good to note a considerable uplift in lamb prices at the summer sales. Increases of over £7.00 per head will have been more than welcome, although it has to be remembered these sort of prices were about in 1986. Nevertheless, it was indeed fortunate that Mr. Fischler's effort's to frighten people off lamb were less successful than this effort in the case of beef.

Despite the dry weather I continue to be amazed how many crops have coped with the conditions. Having recently combined our peas, our crop came out on the right side of 2 1/2 tons per acre, and our wheat looks remarkably promising, but the combine will make the final judgement. Hops, I now believe, are coming under increasing pressure through lack of water in the dry areas, and unless they have been irrigated, I think the crop will be only average. I note the E.U. are now suggesting that pubs should be compelled to sell foreign beers as guest ales. I should think not! The Germans seem to be intent on wrecking our farming industry whenever possible. They should be told in no uncertain terms, to keep their confounded lagers for their own festivals.

Hunts must not take farmers goodwill for granted!

DECEMBER 1996: Importance of landowners

During a recent stay in hospital, I decided to make a careful study of the pros and cons of joining the European Monetary Union. My findings were illuminating, because apart from the obvious disadvantages to British Agriculture, at times when the pound was high, which devalued the conversion rate of the Ecu, when payments are made to British farmers, there seemed to be little reason why we should wish to join. The main reason for joining seemed to be indecisive; the theory being advanced, that, if we did not join we should be left behind. As I could not find an explanation as to where we should be going, it appears to me that if we are going on a journey into the unknown – it is not a bad thing to be left behind. It also became obvious, that few people in the European Communities wished to give up their own currencies. Further, the whole concept seems to be geared to the Europeans, with their inward looking trading, and will be of little benefit to Britain with our larger world markets. I cannot believe that any worthwhile politician would throw away Britain's independence and prosperity, for some impossible dream.

Whilst on the subject of politicians, it is difficult to imagine how some of them could distance themselves from the facts, as they did, at the Tory Party conference. It was unbelievable that the party zealots could propose a resolution congratulating the Government over its handling of the BSE situation.

Whilst it is universally understood that the Government's handling of the disaster had been totally inept, we can only assume that as usual, the politicians and party activists, are totally out of touch with reality.

To return to the real world, we have enjoyed an extremely favourable mild autumn. Newly sown crops continue to thrive and will be in good order to face whatever the winter weather may bring, and hopefully one day, we shall see the ponds begin to fill up. Apple growers have had a good time harvesting their crops and with prices running somewhat ahead of those at a similar time last year, are not dissatisfied, although I understand, heavy imports of Dutch pears are causing disruption at the present time, as we approach mid November.

The beginning of November sees the start of the hunting season and all those connected with this traditional sport will hope for some enjoyable days, with a minimum of interference from the hunt saboteurs. I sometimes wonder however, if some hunting people do enough to earn universal esteem. It does appear at times, some of them fail to realise the vital importance of the landowners and farmers, without whose goodwill they cannot operate. With less and less hunting farmers and now a declining acreage of set-aside, good hunting country is at a premium. Therefore It must be obvious, that the right to hunt over farmland is a tenuous one, and whilst most farmers take a benevolent view of hunting, it must be remembered that there are more efficient ways of controlling foxes, and whereas the sheep may have the golden hoof, the horse certainly does not!

The editor reminds me that this will be the last edition of the South East Farmer before Christmas, and so I would like to wish all my readers a very Happy Christmas with plenty of good Christmas fare and the prospect of a successful New Year. Brook, who will be spending his second Christmas with me, is already eyeing the turkeys with keen anticipation!

Farming at the crossroads

VIEW FROM THE SOUTH
Farming at the crossroad
Sussex champions in We
Southcountry Lamb Ltd
INVICTA
LAMB LTD
Head Office
(01892) 890678

SEPTEMBER 1998: Organic farming

August has always been, to me, a pleasant, satisfying month; the month when all the necessary operations should have been carried out to ensure good, sound crops, and all that remains is to safely gather in those crops – cereals, fruit, and hops – and then start planning for the future.

Unfortunately matters are now less satisfactory, and with farming at the crossroads, farmers face the future with a degree of uncertainty and despondency. The uncertainty springs from the fact that farming worldwide is not having an easy time, and the despondency stems from the fact that the public do not really understand the issues facing farming and the countryside, and the Government would appear not to care. It may seem odd to some readers that I believe British agriculture will never be on an even keel until it has a stable and profitable livestock industry. I continue to hear of farmers giving up sheep and cattle enterprises, while pig farmers are in despair. Horticulturists may query my views, but I believe that farming revolves around the hedges and meadows of the countryside, with horticulture being complementary to the system. Much is talked about organic farming these days; has it occurred to those in high places that livestock farmers

must play an integral part in any organic system?

Sometimes my more pessimistic thoughts bring me to wonder if, in the grand pattern of the EU, farming in Britain has any part? Until the accession of countries from Eastern Europe into the EU and their vast potential for food production, it seems that Britain could be pushed ever more into a corner. I have never understood why we need the addition of further Eastern bloc countries, for it seems we already have enough trouble. Whilst I realise these countries will not go away, with Britain out of the EU it would not be our problem.

Returning to our own problems, the public need to be made aware that farmers and their small force of workers are not afraid to bend their backs, but when their labours continuously result in falling returns, they will continue to give up those enterprises requiring high inputs, with the resulting worries. The whole situation surrounding British farming is a matter of grave concern, and perhaps our farming leaders should consider yet another massive demonstration in London to emphasise our plight. It should be remembered that the knock-on effects of a bankrupt agricultural industry are very far reaching.

As I write this somewhat sombre piece, the sun is shining and the combines are running,

yields of rape and barley are not breaking records and I suspect wheat will be the same, but with good weather we will hope the crops can be harvested reasonably cheaply.

In an unsettled summer many parts of the South East have had below average rainfall, despite some heavy thunderstorms bringing hail to many unfortunate fruit farmers, who will not find the supermarkets in a philanthropic mood. Despite the dry weather, the countryside has continued to look good, no doubt because of the moderate temperatures, July having less than 3/4" rainfall, but no temperatures in the eighties.

After some poor efforts our England cricket team has at last shown some fight and resilience and breathed some life back into what I consider our premier national game. More locally, our Kent team has had a disappointing time and having started the season with what appeared to be one of the best sides in the championship, with trophies beckoning them, it now appears the sideboard will be bare.

Sunnyday is enjoying her first summer at Reed Court and is turning into a good looking, solid racehorse. Brook is fit but will welcome the end of the ballooning season.

GREENFIELDS

SUPPORTING COUNTRY PURSUITS

GUN SHOP - COUNTRY CLOTHING - AMMUNITION
ACCESSORIES - EXPERT TUITION - PRACTICE
CORPORATE EVENTS

EASE THE TROUBLES OF
FARMING LIFE WITH A DAY OUT
SHOOTING AT GREENFIELDS

FREE PARKING – EASY ACCESS
OPEN TUESDAY - SATURDAY 8.30AM - 5.30PM – SUNDAY 9.00AM - 1.00PM
CLOSED ALL DAY MONDAY

STURRY HILL, STURRY
NR. CANTERBURY, KENT
TEL: (01227) 713222 FAX: (01227) 710611
www.greenfieldsshooting.co.uk

Man the barricades!

AUGUST 1999: My stern warning against European Parliament

With the Euro Elections behind us, casting has now taken place of actors for the forthcoming season of Pantomime. We have two new leading actors – or jokers? Mr Kinnock has been cast to sort out corruption and general misdeeds. As he was not a great success at home I do not think he is likely to make big inroads into a mammoth racket. Our Mr Patton has been put in charge of overseeing enlargement of the EU, something that will make Mr Kinnock's job even more difficult.

The Euro elections, if they proved nothing else, confirmed that many people are far from enchanted with Britain's position in the EU and even less with any involvement in a single currency. The election of three UKIP members to the European Parliament and the considerable number of people who voted for UKIP candidates throughout the country confounded the views of Euro fanatics that we are just a small band of flat earthers. What the UKIP newly elected members can do in Brussels remains to be seen; hopefully they will be able to throw a few well-aimed spanners into the works.

Returning to our own soil, I am often concerned about our farming leaders' general acquiescence with the government and particularly Mr Nick Brown. Apparently our NFU leaders think he is a good chap because he thinks they are good chaps. Nevertheless his picture on the front page of

the current summer issue of the NFU magazine does not lead me into raptures. It is my opinion that, like his master Mr Blair, Mr Brown is a considerable under achiever and that he has little to show for his efforts. CAP reform was the usual fudge and now the possibility of a pesticides tax is not, it seems, in his premise, but lies with the environment or the Treasury.

Some of the Draconian rules laid down for abattoirs by the Meat Hygiene Service are out of his hands. Whilst the lifting of the ban on the export of beef is welcome news, I do not think Mr Brown can take much credit for it. Our partners in Europe have just run out of reasons to continue the ill-judged ban. I only hope Mr Brown will be at the forefront of beef producers' efforts to get the export trade up and running again – this in the face of a mountain of rules and regulations which will, no doubt, be aimed at stymieing the whole operation. Finally,

I am not impressed with the NFU's view that we should join the single currency and even less with the attitude of neutrality towards the proposed ban on hunting. If this ridiculous persecution of the countryside happens there will be virtual war by country folk and many farmers, and I shall expect the NFU to be manning the barricades!

Combining has just started in my area and I shall not be surprised if rape, although drilled in many cases in atrocious seed beds, yields well up to expectations. Wheat, which generally came through a very wet winter well, will not in my opinion set many records. Time will tell, and I will eat my share of humble pie if necessary.

Rose enthusiasts who were unable to attend the visit to Rumwood Nurseries, Langley on the evening of July 7th missed a treat. An enterprise that produces nearly a third of a million rosebushes annually has to be a good place to pick up some tips on rose growing and see some new varieties. The rose fields are open to the general public and are well worth a visit.

As we approach the end of the month my wife and I will be acknowledging the fact that we have stayed married for fifty years, and there will be a bit of a party to celebrate. With a steadfast wife, a loyal family, a faithful big dog, many friends and a few horses, what more can a man want!

The Common Sense party

My wife and I have recently returned from one of our quite frequent trips to Norway, where contrary to popular belief, life still exists outside the EC. The Norwegians, a proud and independent people, well disposed to the British, live in a land of majestic splendour and would feel like caged lions to be constrained in the suffocating atmosphere in the EC. There have been two referendums in Norway concerning membership of the EC, both of which rejected the move very much due to the influence of their farmers, who are better led than ours and have no difficulty in seeing the wood from the trees.

Farming in Norway is not easy but where it is possible there is some good land and the quality of their horticultural produce is extremely high – as we saw in the fruit and vegetable markets. I can certainly recommend their cherries. They manage somehow to restrict imports of produce when their own crops are readily available; shades of the past!

When on holiday one has time to think and survey affairs in a more detached way. Accordingly three fellow travellers, not farmers, formed ourselves into a "gang of four" and set about considering how Britain's lot could be improved. It did not take us long to agree that what was needed was a new party to lead the country into the future, and this party would be called the Common Sense Party. On achieving power the first action of the new government would be to remove Britain from an overseas organisation which requires a minimal amount of common sense from its administrators. Goodbye EC!

Other key ministries would be agriculture and it was agreed that besides being Prime Minister I would undertake the full responsibility for revitalising our most important industry, farming. I would work closely with another senior minister at the Board of Trade to ensure that our overall trade would be mainly with the countries with whom we had a realistic balance of payments situation. Next would come the Ministry of Transport, and the minister's particular brief would be to reintroduce electrically driven public transport into the cities and exclude motor cars wherever possible. All efforts would be made to rejuvenate the rail system so that much of the heavy road transport would be carried by rail – so freeing up the roadways and cutting the biggest menace of all, pollution. The final member of the gang of four would be the Minister of Sport, who would be required to take immediate action to improve the state of English cricket.

He would demand that our test cricketers dressed like cricketers and wore their blazers instead of looking like barrow boys on holiday. He would also make sure that country people are able to enjoy their pleasure without interference.

The foregoing may seem somewhat fanciful, but for all my readers who are imbued with common sense I would say: think about it.

Returning to England from a sunny Norway, a soggy sight greeted me, with much combining still to do. At Reed Court we were lucky enough to finish on August 4th. Expensive and prolonged harvesting conditions, together with low prices, do not lead to happy cereal growers. Lamb prices have gone through the floor and a backlog of last season's cooking apples, together with much more imported fruit, is not good news for fruit growers, who must be becoming increasingly desperate.

On the brighter side, for those few remaining hop growers with contracts, the recent rains have been a godsend and those pieces of hops I have seen since my return have shown great improvement. Hops are always a lovely crop to grow as they soon make up time from favourable treatment, cultural and weatherwise.

Home again we do not have a happy farming picture – but we do have a very happy dog!

Planting hop setts with schoolchildren on the farm

Place for all seasons and moods

Following the terrible events in America, with farming at the crossroads and the quite dreadful Margaret Beckett in charge of rural affairs, not to mention inclement weather, my wife and I felt we needed a relaxing day, and so we decided to make yet another visit to Pashley Manor in Ticehurst.

Set in lovely rolling Sussex country, the extremely well preserved Elizabethan manor house nestles down in a bed of trees, surrounded by magnificent gardens. Herbaceous borders abound with a riot of vibrant colours, intertwining with roses and shrubs, all this in the midst of manicured lawns.

The walled vegetable garden would bear very favourable comparison with the great Victorian gardens of the past. The knowledgeable gardening enthusiast will quickly appreciate the cultural expertise needed to achieve the well being of all the plants, whilst ordinary visitors would be very hard to please if they failed to be entranced by the beauty of the place and the friendliness of all the staff.

Sitting on the terrace, I enjoyed a light lunch of home-cooked local produce washed down with some good English ale. I surveyed the lake with the black swans with sheep grazing in the background and

VIEW FROM THE SOUTH

Place for all seasons and moods

By Peter Tipples

South East Farmer - November 2001

Global banking expertise through your local Agribusiness Manager

Talk to one of our local Agribusiness Managers today

You could reap all the benefits that a local bank with global resources can offer. You'll talk face to face with someone who specialises in Agribusiness. Someone who is committed to understanding your business and helping you make the most of its potential.

To find out more, call your local Agribusiness Manager, Stuart Whatling on 01892 531679 or 0207 396 5663.

www.CBonline.co.uk

Clydesdale Bank
Tailored Financial Solutions

wondered if some of the people who make the rules that govern our lives should switch off and enjoy the tranquillity of places like Pashley Manor more often. Their thoughts might be simplified in such a way as to endeavour to make the world a more pleasant place.

Mad world

Returning to the mad world in which we live, I was soon brought down to earth to see the scare stories, based on

remarks by Animal Health Minister Elliot Morley when giving the government response to the report of the BSE Inquiry. These stories highlighted the possibility of BSE infecting sheep and, if this were confirmed, it would mean the eradication of all sheep in the country.

Worse was to follow; a spokesperson for the infamous DEFRA, was reported as stating that she did not believe farmers would mind losing all their sheep if they were well compensated.

Words fail me. Are people like this so far removed from the country scene that they believe that the farmer's only interest in their occupation is the pursuit of money? My father once remarked 'I am not solely interested in money but it's nice to have some!"

Following on from this, the bread makers announced that because of an increase in price of delivered wheat it would necessitate an increase of 20p - 30p per loaf, the increase quoted was £20 per tonne. I would remind readers, that an increase in price of 1p per lb of wheat to the farmers means £22.00 per tonne.

There is no doubt that the producer needs an increase of this amount, but he needs to get it, not those who handle the crop afterwards. I become very frustrated that those who represent the farmers seem to be quite impotent as they let the farming industry slowly die.

EU funds

A good example of this is our inability at present, to persuade the government to take up the agrimoney due the farming industry from EU funds. There is an attitude, that the government must never be pressed too hard, because it is a case of 'never bite the hand that feeds you', even if you are starving!

What the farming industry needs, is for the farmers and their leaders to bang the drum in such a way, so that no one will be in ignorance of the fact that farmers are steadily going bust.

Stop-start

The weather continues to be an enigma these days. The trees are only just showing signs of autumn, when it rains it does not just rain, it comes down in buckets; one week it is cold and at the end of the second week of October the much vaunted Indian summer has arrived. Cereal drilling has been a stop-start affair, but progress is being made. Some of the very early drilled wheat looks very bold – time will prove, if it will in fact get too strong at this stage in the season, but cereal growers will be happier to see it sprouting, as opposed to being in the bag.

Fruit growers have had a good crop of quality fruit and are quietly optimistic for the future. Bramleys that made a flying start to the season, price wise, have had a severe adjustment of this situation, but trade for cooking apples at this time of year is notoriously poor, as barn stored apples are finding their way on to the markets.

Christmas may tell a different story, pear growers will not have to wait until then, they have already reaped their rewards.

With foot and mouth seemingly on the way out, all those concerned with the livestock industry, must press urgently for a common sense reduction in movement regulations, so that the industry can make a real start to getting back to normal; the time has come, to cull the bureaucrats.

The visit to Pashley seems a long while ago, but the magic remains.

Foot trimming

Farewell to a great patriot

With the death of Her Majesty Queen Elizabeth the Queen Mother, the nation has lost a gracious and charming lady, who was also a great patriot, and the countryside has lost a great friend for above all else, the Queen Mother was a countrywoman.

She loved all that went on in the countryside, the wild places, the gardens, the flowers and woods, and the animals, her especial love being horses and dogs in whatever role they were employed. I firmly believe that she derived much of her serene and happy nature from valuing above all the natural things in life, and found peace and contentment amongst real people who abound in the countryside. It has been said that the monarchy are sometimes out of touch with the people. I believe the opposite is true, as the monarchy understands the rural scene and are well aware that the roots of the country are in the countryside. Many urban dwellers overlook this fact.

If real country dwellers really want to pay a lasting tribute to the Queen Mother, they will join forces and fight every inch of the way to preserve the countryside and all its pastimes which she loved. Mr Blair may consider David Beckham's broken toe as a national disaster, but there are many hunting folk who would consider there is a more important disaster looming on the horizon.

There are times when I despair of the general public ever comprehending the steady disintegration of the farming industry. In my own county of Kent, it is even more apparent. Hop growing appears to be almost in its final throes, fruit growers growing Cox on ideal land are leaving the scene and many middle-aged cereal growers and livestock farmers are wondering why they carry on. A point is reached when only so much money can be lost. Kent was known as the garden of England, with its hops and oasthouses and beautiful orchards; those days are gone, it is now the land of strawberries, plastic sheeting and tunnels, and concrete. I wonder if there is anyone out there listening? Because it seems that it is a continuing madness, that one of our great resources – the land – is being sadly underused. To expend fossil fuels importing food from all over the world, to replace food that can be successfully produced here, makes no sense. For those of our useless agriculture ministers, the answer to farming's problems is not to diversify into converting outbuildings to light industrial use, bringing yet more traffic to our rural roads which are, in places, becoming almost impassable.

Some of us do not necessarily have to consult Sir Don Curry to see the way ahead. The application of a degree of common sense would be a great help, although I realise that is an attribute not readily available to this useless urban government.

This time last year we were still struggling with the effects of a long spell of wet weather and April saw nearly 3" of rain. As mid April now approaches, there has been virtually no rain, and with over a week of biting easterly wind, which has dried out the top of the ground, believe it or not, we are saying a nice warm rain would do a lot of good. Generally crops look promising and given favourable conditions, we can look forward to the harvest with some hope – which they say 'springs eternal'.

Easter Saturday saw a fine crowd of cheerful race goers at Charing. With plenty of runners, there was some good racing. My own horse, Peyton Jones, racing under suitable conditions, did not disgrace himself, and put up a flawless display of jumping and helped to make the running until about half a mile from home when the second journey up the Charing Hill sapped his energy and he literally ran out of steam. Nevertheless it was all very exhilarating while it lasted and I live in hope.

The cold wind is doing nothing for the roses at present, but given the rose fertiliser I suggested, and favourable weather, they will look better at the beginning of May.

Perhaps as an all round supporter of sport, I should add that I am sorry for David Beckham and his broken toe, which I hope will soon mend, but I do not consider it a national disaster. Some of us also enjoy cricket and racing!

*Meeting the Queen at the opening of Gillingham Ice Rink.
When one of the Queen's servants was about to put the trug of
apples in the boot, she said "I think we will have it inside!"*

At least a fox can escape the hounds

I believe there is a view in some circles that farming people have a rustic approach to life and are not abreast of current worldly affairs.

Nevertheless, we do have our wider thoughts, and would be aghast at what occurred in the confines of a committee room in the House of Commons recently, in the case of poor Dr Kelly.

No doubt the select committee for foreign affairs would be Labour dominated, and therefore many of those present at Dr Kelly's inquisition would have nobly supported the case of the fox in the recent debate on hunting.

I wonder if they stopped to think that the fox is hunted over open country, with every chance of escape, whereas they mercilessly hounded a cornered Dr Kelly, who had no escape. These are the same people who like to compare fox hunting with bear baiting.

That their behaviour was shameful is without question. For those who think I am always on about the hunting controversy, I would point out there is a message for farmers here and it is not to rely on the judgement of politicians.

At the present time the farming industry seems to be like a pauper, queuing up with his begging bowl at the common agricultural policy reform table. It can be safely assumed that when all the legal implications of this so called 'historic' reform are sorted out – one day – our farming industry will be little better off – but the legal beagles will. So farmers must take the

situation in hand, and deal with it themselves and promote their industry as never before. Go out and put the 'Keep Farmers Farming' posters up on every convenient spot – support the Little Red Tractor campaign, and work to see the farmers markets are a success, and be positive in every respect in standing up for themselves.

What happened in the House of Commons recently is a sad commentary on our present lords and masters, who know little about anything and nothing about the farming industry. There is so much nonsense talked about the environment and the preservation of the countryside when the easy way to cure most of the ills is to see that farmers earn a decent living and with the ability to do that they will look after the countryside as they always have.

With the rape now combined the picture is much as we assumed – very average yields generally, and with a few farmers nibbling at their winter wheat at the beginning of the last week in July, I do not anticipate any records.

However in a difficult summer after a very dry April and below average rainfall in the subsequent months, together with very humid hot weather, crops have generally coped pretty well. With the intense heat wave and dry weather over much of Europe which must badly affect their crops we should be in a position to exploit any shortages.

Any efforts by any buyers organisations to talk down crop prices should be quickly

dispelled, for we are in a stronger position than normal, a seller's market seems to be before us, we must go for it.

For those who make hay it has been one of those summers when you realise how easy hay making is when the weather is on your side. It is nice to note that the livestock industry continues to enjoy better times, for I believe, the basis of a well run countryside is to see the fields well stocked with animals.

On the fruit scene below average crops are expected but only recently I saw some magnificent new season Bramleys, so it seems certain that the farming industry has the prospect of putting some excellent produce before the public who must be made aware of the expertise and care needed to produce high quality food.

My roses are currently in the in between stage, although I have plenty of lovely blooms about. Despite the testing weather they are making good growth and will no doubt put on another good show as the autumn approaches. After the initial early summer outbreak of greenfly, it seems to have died out and with below average mildew and blackspot, there is a temptation to break the spraying routine. Test match cricket is here again.

As I write, South Africa are approaching 300 without loss. Either their batting is better than we thought or our bowling worse!

Traviata roses in the garden at Reed Court

Farewell to two much loved friends

When I wrote at the end of my April article that although my horse was sidelined, 'Brook is sound' I was obviously tempting Providence.

I had noticed that Brook had a swelling on one of his hind legs, which I put down to arthritis. As his condition was obviously deteriorating, a visit to the vet was necessary. The news was shattering, as poor Brook's problem was a malignant tumour, and his days were clearly numbered.

My wife and I were always quite agreed that Brook, who had always been a dignified, happy dog would not suffer: we would do what was necessary. And so when Brook began to lose the use of his leg and was not a happy dog, we said goodbye to a great friend, and he died peacefully in my arms. He now lies in our garden near my roses.

Brook had a sunny nature and loved everyone and every animal. The cats and their kittens and the sheep were his friends. He was also very much our dog, when I was around he was always with me, if I was out, and my wife was in the garden or greenhouse, Brook would be there, and to merely say we miss him would be the understatement of all time.

Reed Court is now a quiet place, no longer is he padding about the house, or helping me drive my farm truck; no longer does his regal bark reverberate across the valley as he took his late evening outing.

Brook epitomised all the good things in life and no man or woman, could have a more faithful loving friend.

To add to my tale of woes, in the same week, I found that my old Point to Pointer, Irish Poacher has passed away in his field. Poach as we knew him, was 25 years old and had enjoyed many years of happy retirement, lovingly cared for by my daughter-in-law.

In his day he was a strong front runner, the winner of five point to points and placed several times; a horse who knew no other but to give his best.

The two animals I have written about, were straightforward, genuine characters who were always the same: Brook's tail seldom stopped wagging. And so this month I have no intention of sullying my article with reference to irrelevancies like the corrupt European Union and the self seeking politicians who drive it along, and will stick to comments on real life. The picture of myself and Brook amongst the bluebells, incidentally in Brooks Wood, is a reminder of a beautiful spring.

A rainy April, until the present very warm spell, has brought everything on: the new leaves on the trees, with all their various shades of green, with a carpet of bluebells beneath them, are magnificent.

With enough rain, there is plenty of grass and although I understand the fall of lambs has been below average, ewes and lambs appear to be doing well. Winter cereals look good and spring sown crops have every chance. Fruit is moving on fast now, and growers will be hoping for a frost free time.

All in all there is a feeling of cautious optimism in the farming industry so it can only be hoped that those who know nothing about farming and the countryside, will leave us alone.

In the real world of action, our cricketers have performed very well in the Caribbean, and in Steve Harmison, provided he is properly nurtured, a bowler to test the best batsman in the world, despite the fact that Brian Lara's 400 put matters into perspective.

The Point to Point season begins to draw to a close, not always blessed by good weather, but there has been some good racing. At the Charing Easter meeting, I was the happy recipient of a bronze sculpture of a running fox, in recognition of many years on the Ashford Valley Point to Point committee.

And at the Old Surrey and Burstow meeting recently Sliabh Foy, a syndicate horse, in which I have an interest, beautifully ridden by Phillip Hall, was a convincing winner, so things are not all bad.

Although I finished rose pruning about a week later than I would have liked, and with cold nights in the first part of April, some bushes have been slow to get away. But with the recent sunny days, they are catching up, and spraying will soon come round again!

Brook

Feeding Irish Poacher

She nurtured the soil all her life

JUNE 2004: Jonathan Tipples remembers mum

By the time you read this we shall know the results of the European elections, so let's make a prediction.

The turnout will again be disappointing, Tony Blair will have taken a kicking for his policy on Iraq and all the parties will say they are happy with the results in the circumstances and claim to be the real winner.

What will actually happen is that we shall end up with the usual mish-mash of invisible people representing very few of us and whom we will not see again until the next election. What I hope happens is that we use our votes to decide where we are going with this Europe thing.

When we first joined we had a sort of temporary membership status, a transitional period – and since then we have become full members of the EU, but we haven't have we? Who was it who said "We are in Europe but not part of it", (or was it the other way round!?)

What absolute rubbish! The time has come when we must decide if we want to be part of a true European state, and with that of course comes a single currency, single tax and benefit rates and everything else that goes with it, or do we in fact not really want to be part of the EU, in which case we leave?

by JONATHAN TIPPLES

Provided we take either of those courses with unity, conviction and sense of purpose we will go forward. We will not go forward if we continue to sit on the fence with none of our leaders brave enough to choose a clear direction. We shall continue to suffer the rules, regulations and restrictions that Europe imposes on us without gaining any of the benefits that true and willing membership could bring.

My father is lucky, because as you will know, he is ver clear which of these routes w should follow which mak for some "robust" debate across the breakfast table, s why is he not writing this ar allowing an alternative view

In last month's South Ea Farmer he reported the sa loss of first his horse a then his dog but now he ha suffered the cruellest of blow For those of you that knew m mother, you will know th she was a lady of simple tast nd she always expressed the wish that when she went she would go suddenly, painlessly and with no fuss – she hated fuss – and in her garden.

On the evening of the 25th of May that is exactly what happened. The shock and sense of loss for us all, but especially for my father, has no bounds.

My dear old mum would have been the first to say that life must go on, and of course eventually it will, but it will never be the same again. This is not the place for the story of my mother's life but let me just say this. She spent her life nurturing the soil, as a child in her garden in Ewell, as a Land Army girl in Berkshire and of course building the garden that surrounds Reed Court today. Now it is the soil's turn to nurture her. God bless you Mum, and may you rest in peace.

Nancy was a great flower arranger. This was her window in St Michael's Church, Marden

Lack of courage loses the day

In the aftermath of the General Election, I have come to the unfortunate conclusion that the Conservatives deserved to lose. Although I have a high regard for Michael Howard, his failure to have the courage to confront the greatest issue of all – our continued membership of the EU, was fatal.

Up and down the country, people voted in their thousands for the UK Independence Party, because, if they were non EU believers, there was no one else to vote for. Although the UKIP did not gain any seats, in many cases they took vital votes from the Conservatives. Why Mr Howard decided to play down the EU issue I have no idea, except to avoid upsetting Kenneth Clarke; and now British industry is faced with continued Euro bureaucracy. Of the rules and regulations bedevilling our industries, the farming industry faces two particular pieces of daft legislation. The waste regulation act that forbids waste on farms, is particularly stupid. Over the years most farms have the odd corner where waste has been dumped, to the detriment of no one. To have to haul this elsewhere, is nonsensical. Secondly, the disposal of fallen stock. Again over the years, especially at lambing time, lambs that have died, were quickly buried, again at no danger to anyone, whereas to have them lying about awaiting collection to some distant place, certainly does pose a problem. I am sure some readers think I am anti NFU, not so, I only wish the organisation would stop acting as an agent for DEFRA and start encouraging its members how to resist, as opposed to comply, with the nonsense, perpetuated firstly by Brussels, and carried on by DEFRA.

May, despite a warm beginning has been a cool damp month, in which I have recorded some rain on fifteen days out of the twenty five so far, but only 0.8". Nevertheless, conditions have been good for growing crops, which nearly all look well. The warm end of April and in early May, should have ensured good fruit crops, but we must wait and see. For stock farmers there is plenty of grass, and so in general it has been a favourable farming spring.

Recently I have attended two notable occasions, one very happy, the other less so. My immediate neighbour's daughter, has just been married, and a truly splendid traditional country wedding was staged. The bride and bridegroom eventually left the reception on a very large, highly polished tractor. It was in every way delightful, although I would have to cross swords with the vicar who conducted the ceremony. In my opinion, the wedding ceremony is a lovely solemn service, that does not require any jokey imprint from a vicar, and there were occasions, as I sat quietly in my pew following the service, that an outburst of applause, made me sit up and think, 'someone must have made 50'! Secondly I attended the memorial service of John Cyster OBE of Northiam. I had known John for some years and anyone who did not know the meaning of enthusiasm, had not met him. A highly intelligent ma which befitted a classics schola his boundless energy, despi health problems, led him into high profile position in the cou tryside. As a young man he rod in point to points and he fle aeroplanes. Then as a farme he was a great promoter of th English hop growing industr he founded a micro brewer and had a pedigree Holstei dairy herd and milk round, could go on, but I should mis something. He was a grea committee man, and a very abl chairman. Away from farming he was an important figure i the Conservative Party, as wel as being a former High Sherif of East Sussex. John was a nic man, who although he had fa reaching ideas, he had alway got time to listen to what yo had to say. His friendly smil and gentle sense of humou marked him down as a ma of great character, the likes o which we shall not see again.

My roses are looking well an thinking of gardening, on th anniversary of the day whe my wife suddenly left her ow beloved garden, for the one i heaven, where I am sure th flowers always bloom; I am reminded, that the Lord work in mysterious ways. Indeed, was fortunate to quickly ge Splash, who is a wonderfu faithful friend, and has helpe to fill a void in my life.

With Splash in Nancy's meadow

Nancy loved Gorillas, when she died we donated £1,000 to Howletts.
Alison is on the left and Linda on the right

Beckett should resign over payments fiasco

APRIL 2006: Month of many weathers

The fiasco caused by the Rural Payments Agency's failure to pay the single farm payments on time is a disaster for our farming industry. Farmers up and down the country are contacting their bank managers to extend their overdrafts, and where that is not possible, suppliers are not being paid.

Whilst this is going on tens of millions of pounds are locked up in Brussels which should be circulating in the industry. One person is to blame for this, and that is Margaret Beckett. When Sir Ben Gill was NFU president, he repeatedly told Mrs Beckett not to apply a hybrid system in the application of the payments, but to base the formula on historic details.

However, Mrs Beckett is a woman of ignorance in farm matters, besides being breathtakingly arrogant, and who knows everything about everything, but nothing about anything! So while the saga drifts on what has happened? The chief executive of the Rural Payments Agency has had the sack and farmers' disenchantment with everything has led to Tim Bennett, a genuine man, being deposed and replaced by Peter Kendall who has a sharper cutting edge as president of the NFU.

But surprise, surprise, who remains? Margaret Beckett, who takes no responsibility for the chaotic situation. Under Mrs Beckett the countryside has continued its downward slide, and generally the present administration has treated everyone connected with the countryside very shoddily. Mrs Beckett, it would seem, with her grand title of secretary of state for the Environment, Food and Rural Affairs, is responsible for the welfare of the countryside. Clearly, her incompetence tells us she is irresponsible and she should do the decent thing and resign. In the meantime, the battle continues to get the payments back on track: interest on the money owed, would be a help.

After a somewhat depressing winter, farmers' morale is generally at a low ebb, not helped by continuing mountains of forms arriving from DEFRA – and in some cases the terrible realisation comes to them, that they are an unwanted species.

March has indeed been a month of many weathers. Hard frosts early in the month were followed by a brief spell of mild weather. But from 11th of the month to the 22nd came one of the longest spells of cold easterly weather I can remember in March. As the end of the month approaches, we are enjoying a spell of south westerly winds, and much milder changeable weather.

It has generally been a dry month, although very recent rain has seen the month's rainfall approaching 1". Rainfall so far this year is about 4" where we would expect it to be about 7". I am not making a prediction, but I would not be surprised if we have an equable summer, with enough rain for the farms and gardens. It seems more that likely that the water companies in the South East will be in considerable trouble, as they deserve to be, for failing to take much needed measures back last autumn.

For what is now a very late spring it is good to see the grass growing again, and sheep and lambs turned out from the lambing sheds should get away well. Although the threat of bird flu will no doubt increase the consumption of red meat and prices in the markets are better, I am still disappointed to learn of people going out of sheep. The idea of more pasture going out of grazing and only being maintained fills me with gloom. I will always believe that a vibrant countryside depends on well stocked pastures.

With the late spring and the hard early March frosts, delayed my rose pruning and I still have plenty to do. But at present they are easy to prune and I have put my finishing date at April 8th. I would add that my rose fertiliser went on in good time in late February!

Our cricketers seem to perform in a haphazard way these days, and be in the habit of throwing games away that by keeping their heads, they could easily win. My other thought is that it is a good thing we live in the age of the aeroplane as they seem to be constantly coming home!

It was 20 years ago today...

As I put my thoughts on paper for the April edition of South East Farmer, I recall that it was for the May publication in 1987 that I began my column. After an introduction about my farming activities and hobbies, it finished with a quote: "He is an indoctrinated anti Common Marketeer." Nothing has changed, and when I quote from a United Nations survey that "the countries in Europe that are the best to live in are Norway, Switzerland and Iceland" and even further only one person in three in Britain believes in our continued membership of the European Union, I ask, why do we not get out?

A lot has changed in the last 20 years, after a longer honeymoon period than I expected, after joining the EU. Farming was beginning to feel the strain. Initially farmers were encouraged to go for full production, but as surpluses began to build up, farmers began to be castigated for producing mountains of food. As I pointed out at that time, it was no good blaming the farmers, they did not mastermind the ridiculous common agricultural policy. They only operated within its rules. The hop industry was already under severe pressure and its death knell had been sounded with the abolition of the Hops Marketing Board, which fell foul of EU rules. I further noted that farmers were beginning to have to cut corners, and some of the jobs that used to keep farms tidy were not being done. And set-

aside was the next thing on the agenda.

1987 was a year of climate ups and downs, heavy snowfall in January was followed by a severe gale in March and a wet miserable start to the spring although the weather eventually cheered up. However, October brought the hurricane and floods to complete an unsettled year.

So 20 years on, in my part of the county, nearly all the hops have gone, as have most of the orchards of standard apple trees. There is not the stock in the fields there used to be, and it has been a changing scene. With set aside coming to an end, and cereals likely to be used more fully for industrial use, the picture is beginning to change and farmers are likely to cease being the whipping boys!

With eight inches of rain this year, it has been a wet time, and many winter sown cereals are clearly showing that they have had wet feet for too long, and will welcome a boost from nitrogen. Rape that never came away as well as I expected in the autumn is an untidy crop. I hope it will improve.

Non farming people often look at me somewhat puzzled when I say a very wet winter is no good to those who farm in the Weald, and never has this been so obvious as at present. After the dry winter of 2006, winter sown cereals never had a check. This year they look tired and are struggling at the moment.

March has alwa been said to be month of ma weathers, as t March has prov After a wet start wh farmers were anxi to get on the land, th w a s some exceptional weath between the 11th and 1 when the wheels could re turn: there was little wind wh made it good spraying. It wa superb time both for farm and Cheltenham races!

Despite what I have said abo the rain, it is lovely to see ditches full and spring flow in their glory. Celandines, lac smock and primroses bring the real message of spring finished pruning my roses the 21st March and have giv them a good dressing of fer iser. Roses put in an outstand performance last year a should be well rewarded.

I am almost afraid to ment the word sport after the events in Jamaica. Bob Woolr was known to many in my p of the world. He was a pleasa generous man who was a g ambassador for cricket and v entitled to a much longer sp of life. His murder was foul any count. On a more chee note, Cheltenham enjoyed reasonably trouble free festi with good weather and go racing.

Before I take Splash fo well earned run, I cannot h wondering how Marga Beckett will cope with Iranians if she could not han the single farm payme system!

*Emily Tipples,
my true mother*

*Sidney Thomas Tipples, Mildred Mary Tipples
(stepmother) with, left to right, Bernie, Stuart and myself*

Pre-war charcoal burning

Carpers are like King Canute

The NFU in its centenary year can rightly claim to have been the prime mover behind perhaps the most successful publicity exercise for British farming, and I refer to the Assured Food Standards scheme fronted by the Red Tractor.

I well remember attending an NFU meeting several years ago, when the idea of promoting a farm assured scheme was first floated. Farmers present were, in general, somewhat cool towards the idea, fearing more paper work, but were generally willing to give it a go. Since that time a lot of water has gone under the bridge, and thanks to a tremendous amount of work and enthusiasm by a dedicated band of believers, the scheme moved on from farm assured produce to where it is now, Assured Food Standards. The organisation, has separate sections for horticulture, combinable crops, chicken, beef and lamb, dairy produce and pigs, all under the assured umbrella.

Whereas in the past those promoting Assured Food Standards were doing their very best at every level to persuade some big names in the food and drinks industry to fly the Red Tractor flag, the position has now changed and the big names are coming forward, asking what they have to do to put the Red Tractor on their goods. Names like Massey Ferguson, Shredded Wheat and Country Life butter are already in the fold, with a big brewer likely to follow. The scheme now fronts produce worth more than £7 billion. With food ever more in

the news, I believe the scheme has achieved outstanding success for British food. To the small band of malcontents who keep carping about having to abide by the rules, I would suggest they are being like King Canute.

After a cold spell in the Christmas season, January as I expected has been a generally very mild month with some very warm evenings: if the ponds did hold a duck before Christmas, they certainly could not have done since! It has also been a wet month with about 3" rain, so the reservoirs should be well replenished after the rivers were in flood. Our weather is certainly very unpredictable, and I continue to be amazed at the speed of change with cloudy weather one day and unbelievably bright sunshine the next: 30 January was a classic example.

Despite the cold weather in the run up to Christmas, it did not seem to check the winter sown crops and our wheat looks very bold. Rape – well, rape looks like it always does in mid-winter. As I drive around the country lanes the sheep seem to be wintering well and there seems to be plenty of grass. I hope there will be some when the spring comes. At the present the farming scene seems to be fairly quiet, with cereal prices holding firm, and farmers facing the future with some optimism. Who knows, perhaps the time is coming when they and their industry

will return to popularity.

The point to po[i] season got under w[ ] in the South East [ ] the last Saturday January at Detling. O[n] day of very favourable weath[er] the going was good and w[ ] supported by plenty of runn[ers] but with a small attendan[ce] The problem with early me[et]ings is they tend to have bet[ter] going than late in the seas[on] but only the real racing enthu[si]asts attend. The racing is goo[d] but the finances are not. M[y] own point to pointer is bidi[ng] his time and looks in extreme[ly] good order – much better th[an] his master as the old cod[g]er managed to slip over on the i[ce] before Christmas and will be [a] non-runner for a while.

As a sports enthusiast [I] continue to be saddened by t[he] conduct of many of the playe[rs] I am well aware that there h[as] probably always been rath[er] more going on in the fie[ld] of action than the onlook[er] realises but there is no dou[bt] that standards are deteriorati[ng] both amongst the players a[nd] even worse, amongst the spe[c]tators. There is no doubt in m[y] mind that the sports administra[]tors have to take a much m[ore] draconian line: forget the mon[ey] for once, and apply the rules.

Recently, the dog belonging [to] a great friend of mine, died – [a] companion for many years, a[nd] he is understandably bereft. A[s I] look at my faithful Splash lyi[ng] beside me, I realise how luck[y I] am. The bond between man a[nd] dog is of a special nature.

Some of the Christmas turkeys I used to keep in 2003

Toffee, the Dorset Down wether cross, in the chicken meadow

OP chemicals are dangerous for farmers

The extensive coverage in last month's South East Farmer of farmers suffering from the effects of using organophosphate (OP) based chemicals, was of particular interest to me. I am concerned that sheep farmers were particularly effected, although this has never been officially acknowledged for a very good, but not satisfactory reason.

If a farmer of his own free will used OPs that was his decision. But in the case of sheep farmers, they were compelled by the Ministry of Agriculture to use OP based dips, in an effort to control sheep scab, and this is the point, that in my opinion, has never been properly pursued. The Ministry of Agriculture knew full well that any admission that OPs could cause health problems would have brought an avalanche of claims.

Because I was absolutely certain of the dangers from OPs, I tried to present various facts, but I always ran into a brick wall. I was confident that these dips affected the operators. But we also had a few mysterious deaths among my sheep, and on one occasion, having had a death in my lambing shed, I noticed there was a very strong smell of sheep dip.

This was so strong in fact, that I decided to send a sample of the wool to the animal health department at Wye College: to my amazement, it was returned with the comment that no smell could be detected. On another occasion I was supplying Manchester University with information on the effects on operators of using OP based sheep dips, to the extent that they paid me a small sum for my help in their enquiries. We had reached the stage where they were going to send a doctor to examine me for any ill effects when suddenly they lost interest. But let there be no doubt that many sheep farmers have suffered ill effects from the use of OP dips, as the evidence is quite clear to see.

If this rather nasty substance had been voluntarily used, I am sure the authorities would have shown a keen interest. As a final comment, the order was that sheep had to be dipped twice yearly, in summer and autumn. As one who had dipped many sheep, they were even more reluctant the second time than the first! I loved working with sheep but dipping was never looked forward to.

As the summer moves on, June seems to be nearing its end very quickly after what seemed a long May. The countryside at this stage gives the appearance of abundance, crops generally look good and at present we are in the middle of some good hay making weather. One facet of this summer is the great quantity of poplar fluff: I have never seen anything like it before, and it has laid on the ground and field crops just like snow: whether or not this heralds somethi[ng] for the future we shall ha[ve] to wait and see. So far Ju[ne] has been another fairly d[ry] month: my recording is un[der] an inch of rain and althou[gh] some farmers feel that a[ny] rain on cereal crops will be t[oo] late, I know it would do goo[d] and hop growers would [be] delighted.

By this time next month t[he] combines will be in operatio[n] and we shall have reach[ed] the stage of seeing how w[ell] our efforts over past mont[hs] are being rewarded. My ro[ses] have been extremely good [so] far, although my favouri[te] rose is still Liverpool Echo[. I] can thoroughly recommend [a] relatively new rose – Chand[os] Beauty, a creamy colour [of] superb substance and folia[ge] with a most beautiful perfum[e.] Whilst on the subject of ros[es] I do not remember ever seei[ng] the wild roses more prolif[ic.] Ascot enjoyed good weath[er] and good racing, and befo[re] we move on to the great test [of] our cricketers, as they take [on] the Australians in the Ash[es] series, we have Wimbledo[n] where I hope our own ho[pe,] Andy Murray, will do we[ll,] although I do wish he could [win] and look happy when he wi[ns.] I am not looking forward [to] the time when he loses.

My horse has now return[ed] and with Splash I am enjoyi[ng] apple feeding time again.

South East Farmer magazine is proud to have produced this book for Peter Tipples.

Money from its sale will go to Barnardo's and National Great Dane Rescue.